D1206446

JACOB DOLSON COX, SR.

BUILDING
AN
AMERICAN INDUSTRY

The Story of The Cleveland Twist Drill Company
and Its Founder

AN AUTOBIOGRAPHY

BY JACOB DOLSON COX, SR.

THE CLEVELAND TWIST DRILL CO.
CLEVELAND, OHIO

LIBRARY
LINCOLN MEMORIAL LIBRARY
Harrogate, Tennessee

41198

B
C S392

HD9703
462
C53

Published on the 75th Anniversary of

The Cleveland Twist Drill Company

PRINTED BY
THE ARTCRAFT PRINTING COMPANY
CLEVELAND, OHIO

COPYRIGHT 1951 BY THE C. T. D. CO.

FOREWORD

By N. R. Howard, Editor, *Cleveland News*
President, American Society of Newspaper Editors, 1947-1948

Jacob Dolson Cox, founder of The Cleveland Twist Drill Company, left to his sons the following extraordinary autobiographical story of his successful struggle to build this company, from which he retired in 1905.

Extraordinary is the term for it. For he was not writing a public record; he was in no sense submitting for anyone's approbation the story of one man's success. He was setting down for his flesh and blood, in the form of a long letter, a chart which he might well assume his sons would find invaluable.

The temptation (and the conventional action since the time of Lord Chesterfield) is to set down rules for life, conduct, and sagacity; to give one's sons one increment of good advice after another. It is typical of Jacob Dolson Cox's insight that he realized that "the story" record of his thoughts and actions, his setbacks and problems and triumphs, would impress far more deeply than all the generalities of advice a father might furnish. We all take advice defensively; but we will strain to hear every word of a thrilling narrative.

Every reader of the narrative will see that Mr. Cox was an extraordinary man. He was a scion of pioneer Ohio stock. He was the son of one of the most idealistic public figures in American history, Gen. Jacob D. Cox, Union military leader, congressman, governor, cabinet member, lawyer, railroad builder and president. His mother's father was the Rev.

Charles Grandison Finney, the early Oberlin College president whose name, as an evangelistic preacher, was for thirty years on thousands of tongues.

In fact, here was a lad who could have been nurtured in surroundings of mild luxury and public affairs, along with the culture with which his parents' vivid personalities surrounded him; who might naturally have been educated at some ivied university for the law, professions, or ministry. Instead, we find him striking out on his own to learn to work with metal and tools with co-ordinated hands and mind, caring for himself without normal youthful demand on his parents.

There must have been strong instinct back of this, a yearning to do what he did. Otherwise, he would have encountered great difficulty in his self-education to become a mechanical engineer, and surely could not have achieved so quickly the inventions and designs by which, while still a young man, he climbed into the front ranks of a fast-growing machine tool industry.

Among his strong native traits, this ingenuity stamps "Dolson" Cox's success in this industrial realm. Witness his own words here. He sets down with enthusiasm, some humor, and the ability to draw conclusions from personal experience, almost all that he did; but it is on reaching the descriptions of the machining and engineering devices which he had to think up to keep his enterprise pushing ahead that the reader will find the maximum gusto, the highest spirit of Mr. Cox's sense of adventure with life.

Some of these inventive discoveries came because he simply had to have them. This is in part an excellent testimonial to man's necessity being always the parent of his invention. An early partner would promise recklessly, to get sales, what this young mechanical imagination could produce. Or many times Mr. Cox would brood over manufacturing's need for a certain better process, and appears to have fairly haunted himself into producing the mechanical answer.

He was a strong character when it came to confronting difficulty and discouragement. In his story, one guesses these incidents are not aggrandized; but, to point up his personal pressures and obligations, his contrivings, his ultimate discoveries of the solutions, he tells about them frankly, and they form a small catalog of all the problems which can beset a struggling industrial producer who weathered three intense depressions. Addressed to his sons, this was his modest way of saying that courage is nearly everything to a man's hopes for success—stand up to your troubles, don't give up, there is always a way if you will compel your heart and your brain to do their jobs.

Another characteristic that stands out here in strong relief is his constant intention to be more than fair with every kind of person with whom he dealt—and in a time when unfairness was far more casual than it is today. He wanted everyone, his employer and his employee, the fellow shopworker, his father, the customer, the competitor, his partners, including "Frank" Prentiss, in whom he found security and comradeship, his friends, and the elders to whom he went for advice, all to know him as a genuinely just and frequently generous person.

He tells here about suspecting his infringement on another's patent, of checking it down, and of sending full notice and a royalty payment to an unwitting competitor. But he does not explain that in that day machining patents were pirated and disguised almost daily and that his act was unusual. In another instance, you find him showing fellow workers that he will do more than his share of a joint task; in another, showing his employer how much more he can produce than is expected of him. His honor about financial matters would distinguish him from many of the easy-going entrepreneurs of his Victorian century.

He could hardly have been his father's son and not have been of this bent. Governor Cox, who seems to have had once to rebuke the boy Dolson for running foot-races barefoot practically on the lawn of the State House where the father presided, was a shining monument of public honor in a time when there befell cynical disbelief about even public honesty. The general was called to cabinet positions at Washington as a sort of token to the people that one upright servant existed, and was regarded as a statesman equally as lawyer and railroad executive. Charles G. Dawes, who studied law in Gen. Cox's office, speaks almost emotionally of his inspiration to the youth of the midwest. And here in his son's private record of himself, the admirers of this great and good Ohioan will find the same qualities of utter independence, of regard for the dignity of man, of never deserting, even for the heaviest expediency, what you believe to be right.

Perhaps the finest thing of all about this direct and humble story is what can be called the story of the free America. Jacob Dolson Cox did what he did because he lived in the air of a growing industrial civilization in which he and all others could plan, think, and dream as they pleased and carry out their plans and dreams to the extent of willingness to work, to think, to sacrifice, and to be unafraid. There were geniuses among the young men of England, Germany, and the other nations of the nineteenth century, but they were not all of them as free. They had great gulfs of class, capital, and traditional domination to try to cross. Here in America, a young man like Dolson Cox never had to limit what he could aspire to do and then work with every sinew and brain-cell to realize.

Imagine the foundation of the modern Cleveland Twist Drill Co. on his original capital investment of $2,000! Did he think how daring he was? No, the Jacob Dolson Coxes of our yesterday did not think it was daring. They thought of themselves—in manufacturing and machine tools, in railroads and automobiles and aviation, in metals, textiles, cereals, chemicals, and the rest—only as being absorbed with the potential of their fields and as having a social and moral obligation to get ahead and not to fail and thus cast reflections on themselves.

They lived in an economy that was free from statist and other outside influences, in which the best competitor won the highest rewards. They understood perfectly that if you built a better mouse trap or a better twist drill, there would be people around you eager to have it. As these pages testify, they also understood that if they could cut the cost of production constantly, the consumer and their own enterprises would benefit alike, and they produced for us today the grandest system of inventive manufacture and lowest-cost consumer satisfaction that the world has ever seen.

They met excitedly and with whole heart the only real obstacle life could present, the free competition of other men's courage and imagination.

This quality is what makes Jacob Dolson Cox's story of his career and his business a thrilling narrative. Let it make you glad once more of our heritage from the men who built up this republic.

CONTENTS

Old Hapgood House, Warren, Ohio, where I was born May 15, 1852

The Little Brown House on the Bazetta Road

AUTOBIOGRAPHY

PART I

CHILDHOOD

I WAS born May 15, 1852, at Warren, Trumbull County, Ohio, in what was known at that time as the Hapgood House on the Turnpike, now Mahoning Avenue. Father was superintendent of the public schools at that time.

In 1854 father purchased what we called the "little brown house" on the Bazetta Road out near the County Fair Grounds. My earliest remembrances are associated with that place. I can recall distinctly the little play house Helen* and I built in the rear corner of the yard.

One morning John and Horace Hutchins came over to our house with a shotgun. I was very much interested to know what was going on, and although father tried to drive me in the house, I would not go, and was therefore a witness to their attempt to kill our cat, which had been giving trouble of some kind. The cat apparently was shot and dropped dead, but as they ran up to it to secure it, much to their surprise the cat jumped up and ran under the house. Father made some remark about cats having nine lives and he supposed they would have to shoot it nine times before they could kill it.

I can also remember distinctly the great snow storm we had while living there, called the Black Storm, when the

*Helen was Mr. Cox's older sister.

Moved into house on turnpike, Warren, Ohio, in 1858

house lights were not visible in the streets. During this storm, when father failed to come home to supper, mother was very alarmed. He came in very late, having lost his way and wandered quite a way from the road.

I can also recall the small, bent figure of old Mr. Hutchins with his old-fashioned long cloak with a cape thrown over his shoulders, followed by the collie dog, Fox, who was a great favorite with us children. Also old Mrs. Hutchins, who used to knit mittens for us boys, and the maple syrup we used to get from the big trees in their dooryard.

Father, having some law business in Niles, Ohio, drove over there in a buggy. I can remember very distinctly this trip, as he took me with him. I can hear him now as he said, "Steady, steady" to the old white horse as we went down the steep hills. We put up at a little tavern, which was right across the road from one of the rolling mills. While father was busy with his law business, I saw the mill from the window. Being very interested, I slipped out and went over to see what they were doing. The whole process was over my head, and on the way home I asked father what those men were doing with those long red ropes. As we rode home he tried to explain to me the process of rolling iron, little thinking that in years to come I would have my fill of that type of work.

Father was fond of botanizing in those days, and on Sundays we used to take rambles up and down Red Run picking the wild flowers, which he would take home to analyze. Those were the days when county fairs were very popular. As we were on the direct road from the town to the Fair Grounds, we boys used to amuse ourselves by hanging on the front fence and watching the gorgeous stages going back and forth and choosing which one we would have. If we could get a few pennies, we were proud as could be and would go over to the Fair Grounds to buy pink lemonade and ginger cookies. For days before it was time for the fair to open, we were all anxious to do whatever we could to earn a penny here or there to spend on that great occasion.

One time after the closing of the fair, Helen and I discovered a hole under the fence and clambered through. We imagined we were discovering an unknown country and prowled around the empty Fair Grounds all one afternoon. There was no place that we could not get into, and we finally discovered in one of the buildings an immense stock of vegetables of various kinds which had been displayed. In triumph we carried home some big squashes which were afterward made into pies.

We were familiar in those days with all the country work. Near us was the Perkins' farm, where we children used to go to get curds and whey. At the Peck's farm we also were always welcome to roam about through the milk house and watch the butter and cheese making.

It was while living in the little brown house that father made my first kite. Kite flying always appealed to me, and from that time I used to spend a good deal of time making kites of various shapes and kinds. Soon I got to be recognized as a kite expert.

The Leffingwell farm was another place where I used to go during vacation or on Saturdays, and was always welcome.

One of the proudest days of my life was when mother bought for me a pair of red-topped, copper-toed boots. I spent most of the first day after she gave them to me going around kicking everything that was loose. It didn't take long until the copper toes were pretty well battered up.

In the year 1858 we moved back onto the Turnpike into the white house built by Dr. Palmer. This was quite a pretentious house for that town in those days. It had a large yard full of fruit trees and a big oak tree in the rear. Just how big this tree was, it would be hard for me at this time to say, but I know as a boy it impressed me as a monstrous big tree. Most of our play hours were spent in and under it. We boys built in the fork of this tree a fine little playhouse. We thought we had a playhouse where the girls could not get at us, but Helen proved to be as good a climber as any boy and we were never able to keep her out of it.

At this stage of my existence, my greatest delight was playing with all sorts of machinery, which I made myself. Numerous steam boilers were constructed out of empty tomato cans,

Mahoning River, where we skated in winter

and our delight knew no bounds when we could succeed in blowing them up. Out of an old clock works I constructed an elevator and used to carry up and down, from the ground to the playhouse, small bits of gravel and other things by means of this elevator. We made water wheels, wind mills and kites without number.

The boys of those days had to invent their own means of amusement. I have no doubt that we shocked our parents by playing marbles for keeps. Mother called it gambling.

In winter we used to spend all the time we could get out of school sliding down hills and "catching on" to passing sleighs, or skating on the river. Back of the Perkins' place there was a large tract of bottom land. The river which ran through this land would overflow anywhere from one to two feet deep, and frequently in the winter it would be frozen over during the high water. When the flood subsided the ice would lie over it in great waves, which made a favorite skating place for the boys. The Barneses, our next door neighbors, had a farm in the country and occasionally used to bring horses to the city. I remember particularly one black colt, which Gene Barnes was afraid to ride, so he got me over there to make the first attempt. I got on bareback with a buggy bridle, and everything went all right for a short distance, but soon the horse suddenly stopped and I landed in the middle of the road. I kept trying until I succeeded in riding the horse anywhere I wanted to go; fortunately, without breaking any bones.

One summer, when mother was away from home and Aunt Julia Finney was looking after the children, we got up a conspiracy and decided we would run away. We took a hatchet, determined to build a cabin, and never go back home any more. We had no trouble in amusing ourselves all that day, building the little cabin out of saplings and things we cut down, but when night came and it began to be still and dark, we changed our minds and hustled back home as fast as we could get there.

A new organ was put in the Presbyterian Church, and since father was leader of the choir, I was given the job of pumping. After I had been pumper for some time, the organ developed a mysterious tremolo. Father and the organist were a good deal disturbed about it, and had the instrument examined by a specialist without discovering that the trouble was due to my "system" of handling the pump handle. By giving the

handle a spasmodic or jerky downward motion, I could produce any kind of a tremolo that I thought would add to the
artistic effect of the music.

'Twas while living in this house that Warren was nearly
eliminated by the Great Fire. We children were all at school
when the fire broke out. The teachers in the upper stories of
the buildings saw how rapidly the fire was spreading, and
school was dismissed. I remember distinctly cutting across

Warren, Ohio, from the lower covered bridge, in 1890

lots as fast as I could run, frightened nearly to death. Great
clouds of smoke and sparks were flying over our heads as we
fled toward home. Will and some of the older children in the
neighborhood were sent down the street at frequent intervals
to report how the fire was progressing. Each report was more
alarming than the preceding one. When the covered wooden
bridge across the river was consumed, the panic at our house
was simply awful, as we thought nothing would prevent the

fire from sweeping the entire street. The next report we got was that the Presbyterian Church at the foot of our street was burning. Cinders and pieces of wood, all blazing, frequently dropped on and around our house. Mother had someone cover the wing of our house with wet blankets. The center part of the house, which was square, had a tin roof, so we did not have much anxiety from that source.

I remember I was so overcome with fear that I was of no use and was greatly in the way, so mother finally had me shut up in one of the rooms upstairs.

Most of the business men, father included, worked all day at the hand fire engine, standing in the river up to their waists

Mahoning River from Quimby Hill

in water, pumping until exhausted. Every few minutes new relays of men would take hold of the pump brakes (as they called them), relieving each other. The ladies of the town prepared luncheons and sent them down to feed the exhausted men. Nearly all the business blocks on Main Street and Market Street were consumed, but a shift of wind in the afternoon changed the direction of the flames and the principal dwelling section of the town was saved. It took me years to get over the effect of that fire, and to this day the ringing of the fire bells brings back to me the terrible fright we went through at that time.

Card playing by the good people of Warren was regarded as a great sin, but boy-like we thought that if it was forbidden, there must be great fun in it. We used to go down to the lower Van Gorder mill and play cards in the corn bins. We knew how to play but one game, and that was euchre. None of us had ever seen a game of cards, and one of the boys insisted that in euchre, clubs were always trump, so we always played it that way. One day Mr. Van Gorder caught us playing cards up there and drove us out with a strap.

One of the amusements we indulged in at the house was playing Indian. In the rear of the grounds was quite a large patch of tall elderberries. These bushes grew up six or eight feet high, with long straight stems. These we would cut off and sharpen at one end. Then we would take our positions and throw them as spears at each other. We carried a short stick in the left hand to ward off those which approached dangerously near. One day, while playing Indian, Will Cochran* succeeded in landing a good big spear right on the bridge of my nose. I carry this scar yet. Having drawn first blood, Will was recognized as champion, but the amusement ceased to have any interest for me after that.

We used these same elderberry bushes for making pop guns and squirt guns. The pith was pushed out with a stick. We

*Will Cochran was Mrs. Cox's son by her first marriage. Mrs. Cox's husband, a professor at Oberlin, died a few months after Will was born.

would then chew paper and make two spit balls. One was pushed about half way through, then the second was inserted. With a quick push of the stick or piston, the first ball would be ejected forcibly with a loud popping noise, and unless there was a good house cleaning since we left, the walls and ceiling of the old schoolhouse must have some of those spit balls sticking there yet.

Right back of our house lived a boy called Fred Newell. One Saturday we started off with Will Cochran to explore the

Deep section of river where I learned to swim

river way up above the old Van Gorder mill. We took off our clothes after we got well up the river and commenced wading down through the middle of the stream. The bottom was of smooth stone, large quantities of which had been quarried out at one place to be used for pavements. The bottom was slimy and slippery. The first thing we knew we stepped off from comparatively shallow water into the deep water known as Dailey's hole. Neither Fred nor I could swim and we went head over heels rolling down through the deep water, with Will on the bank calling to us to keep at it, that we were learning to swim. He encouraged us as much as he could. In a short time Will realized that we were in danger, for he saw that we were nearly exhausted. He then became interested in getting us out, and finally succeeded in hauling us ashore, where I immediately collapsed. It was some time before I could walk. This was about the closest shave to drowning that I ever had. After this I soon learned to swim, but without the family knowing that I went to the river.

One summer evening father thought I ought to know how to swim and took me up to the Kinsman farm, where there was a good bathing place. I pretended to be very much afraid of the water because I did not want father to know that I had been there so many times. He got into the water and told me to come in and he would show me how to swim. I went in pretending to be very much afraid and sputtered and fumed, but finally stepped off and ducked under and dove. Soon I came up beside father. For a moment he was awfully frightened, but when he saw me kicking out as fast as I could, he laughed and said he guessed he had had his trouble for his pains.

We used to have many good times out at the Austin farm, where we were always welcome, but we had to pitch in and help the boys with the work before we could go off to play. They had the largest sugar camp in the county. We went out there whenever we got a chance and became familiar with many of the duties of the farm: sheep washing, sheep shearing, haying, potato digging, corn husking, cider making, and all the various operations that were carried on at the farm.

One incident comes back to me with great clearness. At the farm there was a boy who had come to pay them a visit from some place out west, where they evidently were not in the habit of having many of the luxuries we were accustomed to in our neighborhood. One evening at dinner a large plate of very dark currant jelly was passed around the table, and this boy refused it. Mrs. Austin noticed it and was somewhat surprised that any boy should refuse jelly. She asked him if he did not like it. He said that out where he lived they always threw that away. This was a surprise to everybody, and Mrs. Austin asked him what he meant. He said, "Why, isn't that clotted blood?" Whereupon there was a roar of laughter and he afterward learned to eat jelly as well as any of us.

In the cellar of our house was an old-fashioned Dutch baking oven in which mother used to bake the Thanksgiving pies. Every fall it was lighted to dry corn, apples, peaches, and other fruits. Needing more room in the cellar, this oven was torn down and I was given the job of cleaning the bricks. The mortar which adhered to the bricks was perfectly white and hard as flint, making it necessary to chop it off with a hatchet. In later years I often wondered why it was that the mortar was so much poorer in quality than that used in the old oven. After the oven was removed, we used that portion of the cellar to store wood for the winter. The wood was hauled in from the country in four-foot sticks, sawed up and split in the yard. Then we boys had to throw it in through the cellar window and pile it up. One day while throwing these sticks into the window, we had a match to see who could throw in the most sticks in a given time. Will and I were firing away at the window with all our might when brother Ken threw a stick that did not quite reach the window. He ran forward as quick as he could to grab it and throw it in, when all of a sudden he got a blow on the head from one that we had thrown. The blow was so hard it knocked him over senseless on the ground.

John Crawford, an artist, was one of the peculiar characters of the place. He took a great fancy to Ken, and I think Ken's taste for art was acquired through the friendship of Crawford.

We used to play with the Kinsman boys, and one of the things that amused me the most at their house was a little railroad built of laths, which we constructed under their porch. The road was quite complete for one of its kind, with switches arranged that would work. I used to go down there quite frequently and run cars up and down this little railroad. Henry Kinsman later became a competent railroad engineer. One Saturday, after playing all the afternoon at railroading, Mrs. Kinsman insisted upon our staying to supper. They had hot soda biscuits and honey on the table. I ate so much that I was sick before I got home. From that day, honey lost its charm for me.

The Kinsman boys had a sailboat on the river, that had been brought down from the lakes. The boat was sharp at both ends and clinker built with a centerboard. We used to have great fun with this boat, sailing up and down the river, pretending we were pirates, making frequent raids on the orchards of the people living along the river. Will Brett (Librarian at Cleveland, 1909) and Will Cochran built a rowboat at this time. I accompanied them over to the Spear's planing mill, where they were to get the lumber to do part of the work. Brett's father was an engineer at the mill. I can remember how awfully scared I was when he took me in

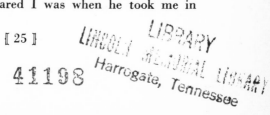
41198   LINCOLN MEMORIAL LIBRARY
Harrogate, Tennessee

where the engine was at work. I was afraid the thing would blow up before I could get out of the room. This was my earliest introduction to steam engineering.

When the engineering work of the Atlantic & Great Western Railroad was being conducted through Warren, I became intensely interested in the building of the bridge across the river just above the Van Gorder mill. I used to get up at daylight, or long before, in the winter months, and go up to the camp where the men were at work getting out the timbers for this bridge. I took great delight in keeping up the fires where the men were cooking their breakfast, and stayed there until school time, taking in all that I could of the processes and methods of joining timbers.

Father must have been serving at this time as senator at Columbus, as I do not recall now that he was at home very much of the time. Mother, I know, was alone most of the time. One day she seemed to be very much disturbed because she had a bank bill which had been pronounced by some of the merchants in town as either a counterfeit or a bill of a State Bank which had failed. I persuaded her to give it to me. As soon as it was in my possession, I corralled all the boys in the neighborhood and went up to where they were building the railroad. We invested it at a small restaurant there, filling ourselves full of lemonade and ginger cookies.

We had to do our own gardening in those days, and mother worked hard to keep us boys at the weeding. She gave me a small patch in the garden and said I could have the proceeds of anything I would raise there if I would also keep her part of the garden in good order. This was my first business venture, and it proved a great success. I planted my patch with summer squashes, and while I took pretty good care of mother's part of the garden, I by no means neglected my own. As a result, I had the best lot of paddy pans and crook necks in town. Since we could not begin to eat them all, I peddled them around the neighborhood and realized $3.00 from their sale, after deducting various amounts of spending money. This money I invested in carpenter tools and began manufacturing bows and arrows, which I sold to the boys. In addition to bows and arrows, one of our principal amusements in those days was slinging green apples from the end of a limber switch. We would cut a good limber switch from a tree, sharpen the end, stick a green apple on the pointed end, and with a whipping motion we could throw them a tremendous distance.

Another favorite amusement of the boys in those days was making small sailboats out of the thick bark of pine trees. We used to get the bark at the saw mills. It would be from two inches to three inches thick, beautiful stuff to whittle. A fellow by the name of Will Dana, who afterwards became head of the musical conservatory at Warren, had quite a large model boat which he had dug out from a soft pine block. I coveted this boat, which was rigged up as a square-rigged ship, and never rested until I was able to earn money enough to buy it. My disappointment was great, however, when I found it would not stand up on its own bottom in the water. This I later overcame by casting a piece of lead which I screwed onto it from the outside for a keel.

There were some tough boys in Warren in those days, two of whom I remember very distinctly; one was Spinney Van Gorder and the other George Gaskil. Lottie Sackett was our teacher at the grammar school, and one day we all had to take our turn "speaking," as we called it. That is, we had to commit to memory some poem or other short thing and repeat it on the stage. When Gaskil's turn came, he pretended to be very modest and demure, but Miss Sackett made him come up onto the stage and repeat something. After considerable hemming and hawing and twisting on his heels, he finally started off talking as fast as he could. He knew he would be stopped if Miss Sackett could get in a word. He repeated the following doggerel:

The cars did rumble, the wheels did squeak,
The steam did whistle, the boiler did leak;
The boiler was examined and found it was rusted;
When all of a sudden, the darn thing busted.

It is useless to say this brought down the house, but Gaskil was obliged to stand on the corner of the platform all the rest of the afternoon.

Miss Sackett was stumped one day by this same little fellow in the grammar class asking her which was right, "clim" or "clum."

During one of our vacations, Aunt Julia made us a visit and undertook to teach some of us children writing and French, but she gave the job up as being beyond her, for we youngsters were better capable of learning "mischief" than French or writing.

'Twas while living at this house that the Civil War broke out, father being away at Columbus at the time. I believe he did not come home before donning his uniform and going into the army. He was commissioned Brigadier General of Ohio Volunteers by Gov. Dennison. In May, 1861, he was commissioned Brigadier General of United States Volunteers. His commission was signed by Lincoln.

It is hard to realize at this time what close economies everyone felt compelled to make during the long years that the War continued. The breadwinners of all the families were away at the front, and the soldier's pay was small, while all the necessaries of life were correspondingly high. We children had not only to do all the work in the garden, but we had to build the fires, put in the coal, clean the walks, and do a great part of the domestic work about the house. Mother always tried as much as possible to make these things in the nature of play. She interested us in drying corn, apple paring, candle making, including the drying out of the tallow, and distributed cracknel to those who liked it. The refuse fats were carefully preserved till spring, when the leaching barrel was rigged up in the yard, the wood ashes brought up out of the cellar, and soap boiling was our Saturday afternoon employment.

At first in making candles we were satisfied with what were known as "dips." These were made by dipping strings of candle wicking into the hot tallow and hanging them on nails until cold. They were then dipped again in the tallow and hung up. We repeated this process until the candles were large enough for use. Later we had tin moulds in which the candle wicking was stretched and the tallow poured in. These made better looking candles and we were quite proud of them.

The Perkinses used to kill a great many hogs every fall. We boys were always on hand, delighted to see the huge porkers plunged into the scalding hot water to loosen their bristles. We were always willing to help scrape them off. For our assistance in this laborious operation we were allowed to have the bladders for footballs. Mother secured as much of this fresh pork for salting as she thought we would need during the winter, and it was packed in barrels in the cellar.

From the kitchen ceiling hung pieces of beef and festoons of sliced apples. They remained there until they were dry. These were the days before the Beef Trust and the advent of canned goods of all descriptions. We were obliged to put up everything of this kind that we needed for the winter.

When Vicksburg was captured, together with the victory at Gettysburg, there was great excitement throughout Warren, and the night after the receipt of the news everybody put lighted candles in their windows. I remember all the front windows in our house were lighted up. For our decorations we got some laths from the planing mill and fastened them across the windows, then we took potatoes and cut them in two. With a tin tube we punched a hole in each potato, in which we set a piece of candle. Four or five candles were placed on each lath and as many laths across each window as we dared without setting them on fire. We thought it was the grandest illumination the world had ever seen. It certainly did look fine to us.

When Morgan made his famous raid into Ohio, the town was thrown into a panic. All the able-bodied men were organized, and the little cannon we boys called the "Baby Waker" was hauled out onto the bluff of the river in front of the Presbyterian Church. Immediately the artillery squad practiced loading and firing. I, with some other boys, spent all of one Saturday and Sunday helping the workmen make canisters in Mr. Jameson's tin shop. We packed nuts and iron scraps in the cans while the men soldered them up. When the excitement was at its height, I rushed to the railroad station and telegraphed father, "Come home quick, we need you here." I never learned whether father ever received this "Order" or not, or whether it was ever sent. It does not appear in his Official Dispatches.

Mother became very much interested in what was called "The Sanitary Commission," which was a society with organizations all over the country for providing hospital stores and clothing for wounded soldiers. Entertainments were given in the town hall to raise money to buy such things as the people themselves could not contribute. I remember very distinctly the Old Folks' Concert given in our town and the peculiar old-fashioned costumes that were resurrected and worn on that special occasion. As my contribution, I collected a great quantity of thoroughwort, which I dried in the attic. Later mother sent it to the hospital because it was considered a healthful beverage. Mother also joined a society called the "Non-Importation League," the members of which pledged themselves to buy nothing of foreign manufacture. The badge worn by the ladies of this league was a stick pin, of black and gold, in the form of a bee.

The Democrats throughout the country were divided into what were called "War Democrats," or those who were in favor of prosecuting the war, and the "Copperheads," or those who were not. The Palm boys in our town were practically ostracized because their father, Jefferson Palm, was the publisher of a democratic paper which was not in favor of prosecuting the war. Among the boys it was an open question whether Judge Burchard was a Copperhead or not. His son, Will, served on a Union gunboat.

The first presidential election that I can remember was in 1860, when Lincoln was a candidate. At this time the organization called the "Wide Awakes" was alive. I can remember the horsemen riding up our street dressed in white sheets, and us boys yelling as loud as we could, "Hurrah for Lincoln." This was followed by "Hurrah for Douglas, and a rope to hang him."

One night mother had arranged that the next morning I get up early to light the kitchen fire and put the teapot on the stove, so that things would be ready for her to get breakfast when she came down. I knew how to make a fire all right, and soon had a good blaze in the stove. Then I put the teapot on after filling it about half full of water. In a short time a peculiar noise began to be heard in the neighborhood of the stove, and, as it was pitch dark with the exception of the candle which I had set on the table, the noise disturbed me. It increased, grew louder and more pronounced, and I grew more and more curious to find out where it was. Finally I made up my mind that there was something wrong with the teapot, and in order to stop the noise I took it off the stove. When mother came down, the water was still cold. Even though I told her what had happened, she scolded me. Just what the outcome of this episode was, I cannot recall, but I have no doubt I got my ears boxed for being such a coward.

It was about this time I got my first knowledge of photography. Will Brett was employed in a photographer's gallery, and having learned something of the art, invited Will Cochran and me down to the studio one Sunday to show us how they made the plates. I believe he was going to take our pictures to show us how proficient he was in the art. He got out the glass, cleaned it with alcohol, poured on the collodion, and then commenced to dry it over a spirit lamp. He probably put a little too much collodion on the plate, for it ran over the plate and took fire. Immediately it began to blaze, burning his fingers, whereupon he dropped the plate and slapped his hands on his pants, setting them afire. About this time Will and I got busy. We poured water on the plate and helped Brett extinguish the fire in his clothes. Then we, all of us, sneaked off home, having seen all we wanted of making photographs by the wet plate process.

About two years after the war broke out, one winter's night, when we were getting ready to go to bed, the smaller children having already been tucked in, the door bell rang. As mother was busy, she sent me to the door to see who was there. On opening it, I was very much surprised to see a very tall man with big bushy beard in a soldier's uniform. He stepped in and asked if Mrs. Cox was home, and I flew off to the nursery to tell mother that there was a big soldier in the front room wanting to see her. Imagine the surprise of the children when the big soldier soon came back into the nursery and routed us all out of bed. It proved to be father home on a furlough.

It is interesting to remember that during the war years my best Sunday clothes were made out of father's discarded uniforms.

My first visit to Cleveland was made at about this time, 1863 or 1864. I had been troubled a great deal as a boy with the earache, and mother brought me up to Cleveland to see if some of the doctors here could not give her a remedy that would stop the trouble. She came up with either a Mrs. Opdycke or a Miss Stevens, I do not now remember which, and as these ladies were relatives of Leonard Case, we went to the old Case homestead and stayed there while in the city. Mother took me to see the elder Dr. Cushing, the grandfather of the prominent Dr. Cushing of Cleveland.

On this trip, I got my first glimpse of real ships and was intensely interested watching them as we crossed the river.

At the Case house I was allowed to put on a pair of roller skates for the first time, and enjoyed the novelty of skating up and down the broad pavement in front of the old mansion.

I wandered down one day to the bank of Lake Erie and sat at the foot of the Water Street hill (now West 9th St.), and my sympathies were very much exercised for the men who were working down near the water's edge. They seemed to be lifting something heavy from the water, but just as soon as they would get it up fifteen or twenty feet from the ground, it would slip off and fall back. When I came back to the house that evening, I told Mr. Case about the difficulty these men seemed to be having in getting what they were after from the water. He roared with laughter at my ignorance, and then explained to me that these men were driving piles for the new depot.

Grandfather Finney's house in Oberlin, Ohio

To me as a small boy, Grandfather Finney was a terrible man. Every time I went to Oberlin, the first thing he would say to me was, "Dolson, are you a Christian?" As I knew very well I was far from it, I would modestly say, "I am afraid not." Then he would give me a long lecture on the ways of the sinner. One time he asked me this question and, as I was tired of the lecture I knew I would get, I braced myself and said, "Yes, sir." I was immensely tickled when he said, "That's right, that's right," and walked off.

At dinner one day he astonished us all by lecturing one of the theological students for eating with his knife. He told

Congregational Church, Oberlin, in which
Mr. Finney always preached

him that a minister should be an example of good manners to his parish. I was sorry for the poor fellow, who was overcome with confusion.

One Sunday while delivering a sermon he described in a most wonderful way a thunder storm. I was so impressed that I could see the black clouds rolling up, the flashes of lightning, and hear the thunder roar. I remember what a shock it was to me when, after reaching the climax, he quietly turned towards our pew and in a conversational voice said, "My dear, I have forgotten my handkerchief," whereupon grandmother handed me one and sent me up to the pulpit with it. He then proceeded with his sermon.

I went out to the Cole's farm once, and grandfather told me I must be sure and come home on Saturday. Well, I did, but not in the way he had intended. I rode bareback into town on an old horse and reported as ordered, but, of course they

Council Hall, devoted to the Theological Department of Oberlin College. One of the corner rooms was finished and furnished by Gen. J. D. Cox

couldn't take care of old Polly, so I gained my point and secured a further holiday by taking her back. She was a raw-boned critter, and after getting out of sight of the house, I got off and led her the rest of the way home.

Grandfather Finney used to take a good deal of quiet

amusement in telling the following story of his early evangelical experience.

He was traveling by the Erie Canal. The day was hot and the boatmen, impatient at some delay at one of the locks, were swearing mad. Grandfather couldn't stand the profanity, and stepping up to one husky chap, said, "My friend, do you know where you're going?" "To Rochester, if this blankety blank blank boat ever gets there," was the reply. "No," said grandfather, "young man, you are going straight to hell." "I know where you're going, you blankety blank blank blank parson. You're going into the canal," said the boatman, and he made a grab for him. Grandfather was a big man and the result of the tussle was, the boatman went into the canal as a preliminary to his long trip below.

After the war father was elected governor, and in the winter of 1865 our household goods were packed and we moved to Columbus. I remember as all the big boxes were standing out in the yard waiting for the dray to take them to the railroad station, father sent me for a marking pot and brush and carefully marked all the boxes in big letters, C.O.D. When the drayman came after the boxes, he asked father what he meant by marking them C.O.D. He replied, "That was for the railroad company to collect the freight on delivery." The man had hard work to keep from laughing, and explained to father that that was not what C.O.D. meant. I have thought many times since that father's knowledge of railroad matters was somewhat limited at that time, and have wondered if after serving as president of the Wabash Railroad he would have marked his personal boxes C.O.D.

When we got to Columbus we occupied the old family residence of Justice Swayne, which stood at the head of State

Street. This was a fine old house, with a nice yard full of shrubbery, and was a lovely place. Father brought back from the war four fine saddle horses, and as the big black horse, Franklin, had a very kind disposition, I was allowed to ride him all I wanted to. As several of the boys in town had saddle horses, we used to ride every Saturday afternoon.

State House, Columbus, Ohio

Sometimes we took long trips up the Olentangie or played tag on horseback in the big vacant lot out at the blind asylum. The man who took care of the horses and the grounds was a convict on parole and a tough customer at that. When the Swaynes went away, they left some guns in the attic of the house and several good dogs. Both the guns and the dogs were sold by this man on his own account.

The boys of Columbus, like those of every small town in those days, were divided into cliques, and it was about all a boy's life was worth to go from one part of the town to the other alone. One day when down at the State House a fire alarm was turned in, and without thinking of the personal consequences, I followed the engine away out into the south end. It was not long before the boys at that part of the town spied me and began to make my life very uncomfortable. Thinking it wise to get back nearer home, but too proud to run, I started up the street pretending to ignore the whole crowd. But just ahead of me I spied Dr. Ide's sign sticking out over the sidewalk, and as soon as I got to the stairs, I bolted up into the doctor's office. He was busy at the time, and I sat there quietly until his patient left. As he turned to me he recognized me and asked what he could do. I told him "Nothing," that I was down in that end of the town and a lot of the boys pitched onto me so I came in for shelter. He asked me if I ran away. I told him, "No, but I walked as fast as I could," whereupon he laughed and said if I could wait a few minutes he would take me up to the State House in his buggy.

As the Governor's son, I had entree to the penitentiary, and it seemed to me that the fellows there did not have such a very hard time. Those were the days of prison contract labor, and I was much interested in the shops where they made harness trimmings, such as buckles, etc. I also explored the kitchen and can remember now how savory the great kettles of soup seemed to me. I thought a convict's life was not only interesting, but an exceedingly comfortable one. While there one day, I inquired for Clingingsmith, who had committed murder at Warren. Mr. Lyman, I believe, was sheriff in Warren at the time this murder was committed and the boys were awfully interested in the tracking and following of Clingingsmith up the river, where he was finally captured.

We boys also explored every nook and corner of the State House. The basement of the State House was a labyrinth of arches, dark hallways, and cell-like rooms. We used to play hide and seek down there, and got to be very familiar with its underground mysteries. One day while exploring, we got into a room where we found on the stone floor quite a pile of ashes. Boy-like, we poked around through this pile of ashes and were astonished to find that the whole pile was made up of burned paper money. Just why this money was burned, I never was able to decide fully, but my remembrance is that father told me later it was badly worn bank notes that were burned to get them out of circulation. I know for a long time I carried in my pocket several ends and corners of bills ranging from five to one hundred dollars.

I was always a poor speller and during one of the quarterly examinations at the State Street School, I looked into one of my books to see how a word was spelled, and the superintendent caught me at it. I presume as the governor's son, he thought he should be more severe with me than usual. At any rate, I was disgraced by being put back a grade. I protested strenuously that I could answer the questions perfectly but didn't know how to spell the word. Helen knew of my predicament, and we agreed that we would not let anyone else know of my disgrace. Together we would try to keep up with the class while I was reciting in the grade lower. At the end of the term my teacher went to the superintendent and told him I ought to be reinstated. He gave me a verbal examination and promoted me. I think this is the first inkling any of the family ever had of the episode. I always did hate written examinations.

One of the social features of Columbus life was the weekly dance at the insane asylum. I remember we used to go up there very frequently on Saturday evenings and dance. The inmates who were ordinarily in their right minds were allowed in the dancing hall, and we used to have great fun. I remember one evening Kittie Mithoff was applauded furiously by the inmates after giving them a sample of the highland fling.

As the Swaynes wanted the use of their house in the second year of father's term, we moved down into Rich Street. Our next door neighbor there had a boy whose name was Dwight Stone. He and I got to be great chums. On one summer vacation we made up our minds to turn the little square yard in the rear of the house into a flower garden, and by rigging up a barrel in one corner of the yard and using some old lead pipe we found around the place, we succeeded in getting up a very fair kind of a fountain.

As there was no yard except this little square place in the rear of the house, most of our playing was done in the street. One day we were playing ball when all of a sudden the ball rolled down along the gutter, into the catch basin, and then into the sewer. I went after it and had no trouble in getting into the sewer, but I did have considerable trouble in getting out again. Finally after much difficulty the boys reached down into the catch basin and pulled me out.

Often for exercise and fun we used to race the length of the block. A colored boy who was there one day proved to be the swiftest footed of the whole bunch, but I insisted that I could beat him if I could go barefooted, whereupon I was challenged. The race was on, I took off my shoes and stockings, ran the length of the whole block and beat him. Just as we came up to the line puffing and hot, father turned the corner. He took me by the collar and marched me off home, reprimanding me for running races barefooted with a negro

boy. My only excuse was that I had been challenged and I
was bound I would not be beaten.

In the spring of 1868, father moved to Cincinnati, taking a
house on Dayton Street. He resumed the practice of law and
had for a partner General Henry L. Burnett. By this time I
was in the upper grades and was sent to Hughes High School.
Before leaving Warren I had contracted a persistent case of
chills and fever, and seemed to grow worse in Cincinnati
rather than better. I was very irregular at school, there being

General Cox's house in Cincinnati

many days when it was impossible for me to go. I was tall
and slim and yellow. At Hughes High School the boys used
to pick on me a good deal, and one day I was getting the
worst of a skirmish in the yard. At this point a big fellow by

the name of Jim Cullen, who was in our class, grabbed the fellows that were on top of me, jerked them off, pulled me out of the ashes, and told me to go in the school house, that he would take care of the crowd. Ever since I have had a warm spot in my heart for him.

Years later Jim went to a Polytechnic Institute and from there moved to the Niles Tool Company at Hamilton. By 1905 he was superintendent and general manager of that large institution.

I remember mother had a pretty hard time during our residence on Dayton Street. Brother Ken had not been well for a year or more, as he was suffering with a tumor on his face. This had been treated regularly with iodine, and the doctors had led us to hope that it would in time be absorbed. But it grew and grew until it was about as large as your fist. To add to mother's care and trouble, Col. E. A. Tracy, a member of father's army staff, arrived at our house suddenly with his wife and daughter. He was evidently dying with consumption and had to be carried into the house. Mother had our front parlor turned into a bedroom for his special use, and disposed of the other members of the family as best she could. The colonel was very irritable and very hard to please. He would demand all the luxuries that were hardest to get, and mother was at her wit's end trying to make him comfortable, knowing that he would probably never leave the house alive.

It was during the time when she was so occupied with the colonel that Ken's trouble developed a new and startling feature. We were playing upstairs when Ken suddenly gasped and began to bleed profusely from his mouth. The hemorrhage was severe and it left him very weak and pale. I thought

Ken was going to die right on the spot. I ran for mother, who of course was very much frightened and rushed me off for the doctor. Ken was subject to frequent hemorrhages after this and his strength was very much depleted. This continued and a few years later, when father was Secretary of the Interior, Dr. Mussey of Cincinnati performed an operation as a last resort. They all thought that Ken would die under the operation, but they also felt sure that he would die if they did not perform it. The operation was performed February 20, 1869. It was successfully carried through, and Ken regained his health as well as considerable weight.

In January, 1869, I was sent to Oshkosh, Wisconsin, mother thinking that the northern climate would be much better for me than that in Cincinnati. When I left home to go to Oshkosh I voluntarily gave mother a written promise I would not use tobacco or any strong drink until after I was twenty-one years old. I lived up to the promise conscientiously.

I had a letter of introduction to an old army friend of father's in Chicago, whose name I have forgotten. When I arrived at Chicago I took a carriage and went to the gentleman's office. He treated me nicely, took me out to lunch, and that evening saw me on the train which was to take me to Oshkosh. That night it was very cold and there was a tremendous snow storm, so the train was delayed several hours en route. We did not get into Oshkosh until about midnight. There was no one there to meet me and no carriages but one omnibus, which I climbed into, telling the driver I wanted to go to the house of C. G. Finney. He said he knew where it was and would take me there all right. No one was up in the house when I got there. My baggage was dumped off in the deep snow, and, by repeated pounding on the door, I finally aroused Uncle Charles, who let me in. He did not seem to be altogether pleased at being routed out of bed at that time of the night, but I had reached my destination and Aunt Angie was like a mother to me. They lived in a one-story cottage house with a large yard, which had recently been planted with young trees.

When hunting a year or two before, Uncle Charles received a very bad gunshot wound. While leaning on his gun, it discharged and the bullet went through the center of his right hand, broke the bones in his left forearm, and went through his neck. As a result he was badly crippled. He had brought back from the war his favorite saddle horse, which he kept in the barn, but for a year the horse had never been cleaned. The horse's hair was matted, full of dust and dirt, and he was a sorry looking animal. I was told that if I would clean the horse and feed him I could ride him all I wanted to, which bargain I was not long in accepting. In a short time I had him as sleek and handsome as could be and was spending my afternoons roaming over the country on horseback. The heavy snow which had fallen the night of my arrival was soon crusted over by the hot bright sun and cold nights, so that the crust was strong enough to bear the horse, and all winter long I led him on this crust from the barn to the house whenever he needed to be watered. There was so much crusted snow that we could skate for miles over the country on it.

The Lake of Oshkosh, Winnebago, was frozen over, and so strong was the ice that teams crossed and recrossed it in various directions, there being regular roads over it. The winter was long and severe, but when summer at last came, it seemed to leap from snow and ice into green grass and flowers.

In the spring Uncle Charlie got me passage on a tug boat that was going down the Fox River for lumber. This was a very pleasant trip and I learned considerable about machinery, rafting, etc., before we returned. The tug was a shoal draft, side wheel steamer. The rope that the towing was done with was coiled up on a big drum just aft of the engines. The boat was not powerful enough to tow the big raft of lumber in the ordinary manner, and the way they accomplished it was this. The men would fasten the end of the rope to the raft and then steam ahead, unwrapping the rope from the drum as they progressed, until they got to the end. Then they anchored the tug by dropping a large vertical timber which stood in the bow of the boat. This timber was iron shod on the end, and by its great weight buried itself deep in the bottom when dropped. This timber was called a "grouser." The boat thus securely anchored would slowly wind in the rope, drawing the lumber raft up to it. This operation was repeated again and again. This was slow progress, but for me it was lots of fun.

James Atkinson lived at Appleton, a few miles down the river, and during the winter I went down there for a short visit. While there Mr. Atkinson thought I might be of some use to him, and gave me a book in which were the measurements of many thousand feet of lumber. My job was to add up these long columns of figures, the object being to find out how much lumber he had in his yard. I can still remember how disgusted he was, after going over some of my work, that the columns of figures had not been added up correctly.

When sliding down hill one day, I severely sprained an ankle and was kept there very much longer than I had expected. There was a strong revival going on in the village of Appleton, and as all the Atkinson family were deeply religious, I was persuaded by them and Jennie Bushnell that it was my duty to join the church, which I did.

Next door to Uncle Charlie's lived a Mr. Sanford and his wife with one daughter, Zulika. Mr. Sanford was the owner of a very large blacksmith shop where I used to love to go and spend considerable time watching and helping the men. They not only did horse shoeing, but also a great deal of heavy blacksmith work, forging, etc., for the saw mills of that district. It was in Mr. Sanford's shop that I first learned to use the sledge hammer. Mr. Sanford seemed to be very fond of me, and I certainly was of him, and used to spend many evenings over at their house visiting. Almost every Sunday night I used to go over there and crack hickory nuts and chat with them. This acquaintanceship led later on to the making of pleasant friends in Cleveland, as the Sanfords were related to the Binghams.

Winter storage of ore ships in Cuyahoga River

PART II

LEARNING A TRADE

IN the summer of 1869, I went to Oberlin and, paying my tuition in advance, entered the Commercial School there. I had hardly begun my studies when I received a letter from mother saying that through her efforts I had been offered employment by the Cleveland Iron Company, and that I should go right to Cleveland and report for duty there. I tried to get the school principal to refund the money which I had paid, but this he refused to do, so I left Oberlin (August 15) on the early train and arrived in Cleveland at six o'clock in the morning. Immediately I went over to the mill, arriving there before the men were ready to go to work. Mr. Joseph Ingersoll, who was the superintendent and general manager, found me there when he came down and took me out into the mill yard to show me what I was to do. My duties were to weigh the iron ore as it was taken from the vessels and enter the weight of each barrow full in a book. These weights were added up later, and the ore company was credited with the total as shown by the mill scales.

In view of the wonderful facilities for unloading vessels now in use in Cleveland and other lake ports, a description of the crude appliances we worked with in those days will be interesting.

The iron ore was brought down from Lake Superior in two-masted schooners. The two finest schooners on the lakes that season were the Eliza Gerlach and the Oliver H. Perry. Their maximum load was 500 tons. When the boat was ready to be unloaded, a block was suspended by ropes from the mastheads over each of the two hatches. A rope passed over this block and down into the hold, and on the end was suspended a wooden bucket, holding from 500 to 1000 pounds. The other end of the rope passed under a snatch block attached to the edge of the dock. To this end of the rope a horse was hitched. A boy led the horse back and forth, up and down the dock, lifting the bucket as he led the horse forward, and dropping it into the hold as he backed up. A staging was erected on the edge of the dock on which two men were stationed to dump the buckets into wheelbarrows. A runway of planks was built from the staging on the dock back to the ore dump, and two men with wheelbarrows operated on each runway. This arrangement entailed the labor of four men on each runway and a horse and boy on the dock, making ten men altogether. Besides the men in the hold who shoveled the ore into the buckets there were also two horses. All the men working in each hatchway were called a gang, and the two gangs working ten hours a day under favorable conditions could unload a 500-ton schooner in from five to six days.

As a matter of interest, by 1905 a steamer carrying from 1500 to 1800 tons could be unloaded in Cleveland in scarcely more than five or six hours.

Each wheelbarrow full of ore taken out of the vessel was run onto an ordinary pair of scales near the dump and weighed, and my business was to enter this weight in a memorandum book so that the net amount of ore delivered could be ascertained. After many experiments, I found that the most comfortable seat I could arrange at the scales was a nail keg with the head knocked out. We had to sit outdoors in all kinds of weather, rain or shine, ten hours a day, and the job soon got to be very tedious. In rainy weather I kept my count on a shingle and transferred it to the book in the evening. Sometimes the monotony was broken by the shifting of the gang planks or the arrival of a new ship, when the whole staging and the gang planks had to be rearranged to accommodate the change in vessel. One day after I had had some experience as weigher, and the staging and planks were being rearranged, I made some suggestion as to the arrangement of the planks to better accommodate the passing of the wheelbarrows going to and from the vessel. As the gang employed at this kind of work was of the roughest kind, my suggestions were received by part of the gang with curses. However, a big Irishman, who was sort of a leader in the gang, appreciated the advantages of my suggestion and immediately turned upon the balance and told them that I had more brains than the whole lot of them. He told them further that if they did not do what I told them, there would be a fight. This settled the question and tickled me immensely. After that I was always boss when there were any changes going on.

I worked my first day at the mill without any lunch. I had made no arrangements for getting a lunch, nor had I selected at that time a boarding house, having reported at the mill directly from the train. In the evening I went to the house of Mrs. Hapgood, who kept a boarding house at the corner of Superior and Erie (now East 9th) Streets. Mrs. Hapgood was from Warren, and as we knew the family very well, I had no difficulty in getting fairly good accommodations there. The house was crowded, and I was obliged to take a room with Charlie Fuller.

The Hapgood house was full of very nice people, and the acquaintances I made there have been some of the most pleasant of my life. Among the young people were Mr. D. Z.

Norton and his brother John, Horace Corner, Jim Cogswell and his brother Albert, George Schryver (who afterward married Fannie Hapgood), Mr. and Mrs. Fuller with their children Charlie and Fannie, Mr. and Mrs. John Hutchins and their daughter Nellie, Mr. and Mrs. Linus Austin, and the two Misses Baron.

With this house full of young people, and other friends, I soon had quite a large acquaintanceship.

I joined the Third Presbyterian Church, where the Fullers and Hutchinses were members, and became active in Sunday School work.

As work on the ore dock grew slack in the fall, I spent a good deal of time in the office of the Cleveland Iron Company, helping the bookkeeper with his payroll, and frequently accompanied him from the office to the bank and back when he went after the money for the men. At the close of navigation, I was put in what they called the scale house, which was a little office near the main entrance to the mill. Here all of the coal and pig iron delivered to the mill were weighed and charged up to the furnace to which it was delivered, and on these scales was also weighed all the iron delivered from the mill.

During the Christmas Holiday of 1869, I got permission to go home for a visit. Father was then Secretary of the Interior and lived on Jersey Avenue in Washington. The family was all at home when I got there, and we had a jolly time. Will had rigged up in the attic a little billiard table and we had lots of fun evenings playing billiards. We also amused ourselves with dumbbells. One evening Will was swinging these dumbbells when one of them slipped out of his hand and went flying out through the window and down into the rear yard. Another evening when there was some bantering going on among the young people I told Will that when I was a boy he had teased me many times up to the limit, and I had always said that when I got big enough I was going to lick him. I thought that now I was able to do it. This led to a little scuffling, and I finally picked Will up, carried him upstairs, laid him down on the bed, and left him there after giving him a good spanking. Since that, Will has been very respectful.

When my vacation was over, I bought a ticket on the limited back to Cleveland and left Washington about seven or eight o'clock in the evening, bidding the family good-bye. My ticket called for a change of cars at a junction some miles out of Washington. Very soon after starting, the brakeman opened the door and sang out some junction or other, whereupon I jumped from my seat, ran to the door and asked him if this was where I changed cars. He said, "Yes," and I climbed out on the platform. When the train pulled out there was no sign of a town anywhere about. I stepped into the station and asked one of the employees when the train would come along that was to take me on my journey. The man looked at my ticket and said, "You have gotten off at the wrong place. There is no other train through here to-night." After thinking the thing over for a few minutes, I said to him, "I don't see any place where I can stay overnight. Is there a train through here soon that goes back to Washington?" His reply was, "Yes, in about an hour." When the train came through I got on and went back to Washington, arriving at the house about midnight, very much to father's surprise. This, so far as I know, is the only time that I ever made such a mistake.

In the spring of 1870 Mr. Ingersoll came to me to find out what I wanted to do ultimately. He asked me whether I wanted a position in the office or whether I wanted to learn the practical side of the business. I told him I had no taste for office work but would like very much to become a practical rolling mill man. He said to me, "If that is the case, then the place for you is in the mill, and I think you had better start in the machine shop." This was perfectly agreeable to me, and in a few days, after someone was secured to take my place, I went into the machine shop.

The foreman or superintendent of the machine shop, who had charge of all the engines, boilers, and other mechanical appliances throughout the mill, was a man by the name of Ben Bourne. Mr. Bourne was a man about fifty years of age, a good mechanic, and a thorough gentleman. They put me at work in one corner of the little machine shop on a rickety old machine tapping $\frac{1}{4}$ inch nuts. This was a nasty, dirty job and they kept me at it till I was thoroughly disgusted. They brought the nuts into the machine shop a few kegs at a time, and each time they brought in a few kegs I thought this was the end of the job, but no sooner would I get them all tapped when another lot would be brought in. After working at this machine for some weeks, I went to Mr. Bourne and told him that I guessed I knew as much about tapping nuts now as I ever would and I wished he would see if he could not give me another job. He smiled and said he did not blame me for wanting a change and he would see what he could do. In a few days I was taken off nut tapping and given a lathe to run. This was an old-fashioned twenty-inch swing lathe with a very long bed, evidently put into the machine shop with the intention of turning shafting. The lathe bed was made of two wooden timbers with iron straps screwed down on the top surface to receive the tail stock and carriage. It was a very crude affair, but to me it seemed like a great promotion. I did various odd jobs on this lathe, such as boring out the big bevel gears for the squeezers. These gears were about nineteen inches in diameter at the largest part, and the hole through them was about ten inches in diameter and eighteen inches through. This gear went on the end of a shaft under the rotary squeezers and drove the machine round and round. As the slag from the puddled balls which were put through the squeezers ran out at the bottom and dropped onto the big bevel gears, the gears were rapidly worn out and it pretty nearly kept this lathe busy boring out new ones.

One day Mr. Bourne had brought into the shop a big pulley about four feet in diameter. He had it rolled up beside my lathe and said to me that he had to go up town immediately, but he wanted me to see if by any means I could rig up my machine to bore out the hole in that pulley. At first it seemed to be an impossible job, but after a little thinking, I unfastened the head stock of the lathe from the bed and turned it round end for end so that the face plate hung over the end of the bed. This allowed the lathe to swing as big a pulley as would reach from the center to the floor. This was considerably more than the diameter of the pulley on hand. I then got some blocks to make a support for the lathe carriage. I took the carriage off the lathe, placed it on the blocks on the floor in front of the pulley, then got two pieces of wood about four inches square, long enough to reach from the ceiling down to the carriage. I fastened the carriage securely in place by driving wedges under the ends of these square timbers, and succeeded in boring out the hole very satisfactorily by feeding the tool through by hand. This operation required a good deal of care and very close attention in order to get the hole straight and smooth. Any irregularity in the feeding of the tool, either taking more or less of a cut at any one time, would produce a ridge or mark in the hole.

We had a Yankee machinist in the shop who was very skillful in boring holes for a running fit, driving fit, or shrink fit. I asked him one day what rule he had for making the proper allowance, so as to be sure of getting the desired kind of fit. "Rule!", he said. "I ain't got no rule. I jest guess at it, but I'm a pretty damned good guesser." This was his way of saying it was a question of judgment acquired by experience.

This was only one of many instances where the tools in this machine shop were wholly inadequate to perform the work required, and the men were constantly called upon to exercise their inventive faculties to get out the required work.

As I had a good deal of leisure time when running a lathe or planer on a job which did not require constant attention, I filled in such odd moments by making a set of tools for myself. I made a chipping hammer, a steel square, a straight edge, and several sizes of calipers. All of these tools were pronounced by the men in the shop to be first-class in every respect. I used them constantly for several years and never had any occasion to find fault with them.

There was a large blacksmith shop in connection with the mill, the foreman of which was Harlo Hiems. He was a splendid fellow of the New England type of blacksmith, and any forging I wanted done he was always glad to do for me. As it was necessary for me to go to the blacksmith shop very frequently with tools and other things to be forged, I used to amuse myself while waiting for the work by helping Hiems.

I got to be quite expert with the sledge hammer, and was very proud when one day Mr. Hiems allowed me to "strike" for him with two other blacksmith helpers. The three of us stood round the anvil and with a long swinging blow would strike in rotation.

I did all kinds of work in the mill machine shop and I doubt if in any other place I could have had such an all round experience. I was changed from the lathe to the planer, then to the drill press, and then onto vise work. As I was always handy with my hands, I was interested in all of the work and soon became quite an expert vise hand. In those days we had to do an immense amount of chipping and filing. Sometimes we would get a job where we would have to chip with hammer and chisel for days at a time. On such jobs I learned to rest myself by swinging the hammer with the left hand, and I was the only man in the shop who could do it. This trick came in very handy at one time. They broke a collar on one of the large rolls in the bar mill and they wanted it fixed without taking the mill all apart, which was a heavy job. With great pride I set to work chipping out the broken collar which had to be done by lying down on the floor and chipping with my left hand. It took three days to get the roll in condition for the insertion of a piece which I afterward planed on the planer and then fitted into the recess I had already prepared for it. I accomplished this job so nicely that the new piece had to be driven into place with a heavy sledge. This made the roll as good as new.

The machine shop was at the end of a long one-story building, which was devoted to the manufacture of nails. This was about the noisiest place one could get into. I do not remember now how many nail making machines were running in this room, but I should estimate that there were in the neighborhood of thirty or forty. The biggest machine was nearest the machine shop, and on this machine they made twenty-penny spikes. The roar of these machines when in operation was so great that we were obliged to shout at each other at the top of our voices in order to be heard. It was in this nail mill that the first barbed nails were made. These nails were called the Winslow Barbed Nails and were mostly used for fastening down the tops of railroad freight cars.

After I had been working in the machine shop some months, I was put in charge of all of the shears throughout the mill. These were immense machines for cutting off bar iron, either hot or cold. The largest one was run by a separate steam engine and would cut off a bar of cold iron eight inches wide and an inch thick. My job was to see that all these machines were kept in running order and that extra knives were on hand and sharpened ready for the men to change at any time, when those in use became dull. Nearly always the men in charge of the shears would come to me before the knives were changed. I had to see that the orders were given for new knives at the blacksmith shop and that they were always ready and properly tempered and the holes drilled in them for the retaining bolts. In looking after this job, I acquired a good deal of experience in the forging and tempering of steel.

My next job in the mill was to take care of all of the steam and water piping. If there was any trouble anywhere in the mill with water stoppage or water leakage or steam trouble, I was sent for to correct the difficulty. As much of this piping was directly over the furnaces, I often had a boy pour water over the planks on which I was standing to keep them from blazing. This experience in the handling of piping was in later years a great help to me, as I was thoroughly familiar with all kinds of pipe fittings and the methods of putting pipe together and taking it down.

At one time I was set to work with some other men to chip out the scale on the inside of one of the big boilers. These boilers were heated by the waste gases from the blast furnace. We had not been at work very long in this boiler when we began to feel sick. We clambered out of the boiler through the man-hole on top as fast as we could, but one poor fellow fainted before he could get out. The foreman called for a volunteer to go down into the boiler and help him. I offered to undertake the job. I climbed back into the boiler, passed a rope under the man's arms, and they started to pull him up, but he was so limp that his head hung down and caught under the edge of the boiler. It was only after several trials that I succeeded in holding his head up straight until they got him started up through the hole. I shall never forget the feeling that came over me when I found that I was in the boiler and this fellow might stick in the man-hole and I would be smothered.

In addition to these regular duties, I was called upon many times to help in other work which might be going on in the mill, as there were frequent breakdowns. One St. Patrick's Day, late in the afternoon, they broke a big bevel gear on a squeezer, and as there was no new one ready to be put in, I was set to work boring out a new one. This was a long job and I worked at it steadily all the rest of the afternoon and evening. When I had finished, all hands were called to dismantle the squeezer, get off the old pinion, and put on the new gear. It was a bitter cold day and the only fire we had to keep ourselves warm was a coal fire in a piece of boiler shell set up on legs on the mill floor. This job took us just thirty-six hours from the time we started until we finished, and none of us left the mill during that time. At the end of it I was pretty nearly frozen to death and never wanted to undertake a similar job again.

I was very much surprised one day to have Mr. Ingersoll come into the machine shop and take me out into the mill to weigh iron. It was the custom to take the hot iron from the rolls to the shears and shear it into lengths. Each piece as it dropped from the shears fell into a buggy. These buggies were run by boys onto a pair of scales and then out onto the dump. The men at the rolls were paid for their work by the record of these scales. I noticed as soon as I commenced to weigh this iron that there was considerable excitement among the men at the rolls and they watched very closely every buggy full that was weighed.

I was only kept at this job a few days and it was not until several years later that I learned that the young man whose place I had taken had been falsifying the weights, and the men at the rolls had been paid more than their legitimate wages, sharing the overpayments with the young man at the scales. At inventory time the management of the mill discovered that the amount of iron on hand was far below that which their books showed they ought to have, and suspected that something was wrong. As a check, the boss had me operate the scales to see if the weights had been returned correctly.

At one side of the machine shop were two roll turning lathes. In charge of these machines was a man by the name of Bill Edmondson, who had working for him a young fellow

by the name of Billy Urquhart. His job was a very peculiar
kind of work that interested me very much, so Billy Urquhart
and I got to be great friends, as I would slide over there at
every opportunity to watch him and visit with him.

Billy was a great smoker and always had a pipe in his
mouth. I was under promise not to smoke, but I did like to
sit down beside Billy and get a few whiffs in my face.

I cannot recall at this time in what year it was that the
mill burned down. It must have been 1871, for I find by my
expense book that I drew my last pay from the Cleveland
Iron Company on February 15, 1871, and drew my first pay
from the Cuyahoga Steam Furnace Company, April 2, 1871.

Blast furnace on the Cuyahoga River

One day as I was going through the mill, I noticed a tremendous flash of cinders from the rail mill shoot up into the roof
of the mill. In a moment the roof was on fire and the flames

spread with lightning rapidity. My first thought was to seize a bucket and try to climb up to the burning spot. Before I could get half way up, it was too hot for me and I was forced to go back. I then ran as fast as I could to the machine shop to get my belongings, as I saw that the mill was doomed. My bursting into the machine shop was the first intimation that the men in that quarter of the works had that there was any fire. I urged them to hurry all they could to get out their effects, and proceeded to pack up my belongings, but in spite of the haste which we made, I was forced to leave the building before I could change my shoes. In the mill I always wore hob nail shoes made from heavy cowhide to protect my feet from the hot plates and furnaces, and I was obliged to fly from the building after changing only one shoe. The mill was entirely consumed.

A few days after the fire I applied for work at the machine shops of the Cuyahoga Steam Furnace Company, which was across the river at the foot of Detroit Street. This was the oldest machine shop west of Buffalo and they made everything in the line of machinery and steam engines. The company was managed by Mr. J. F. Holloway, who was a mechanic of unusual ability. Shortly before his death he was elected president of the American Society of Mechanical Engineers.

I was given a great variety of work in this shop and learned to read drawings and work from them. The shop was three stories high. As it was in the side of a hill, the lower floor was on a level with the docks, while the second floor was on a level with Detroit Street. In the basement or lower floor were the heavy large machines, the largest that I had ever seen at that time. On the second floor were the lathes, drill presses, shapers, and other light tools. On the third floor were the pattern loft and pattern shop. This company not only had a machine shop, but a foundry in which they made their own castings, and while at work there I learned a great deal about foundry methods and pattern making. Most of the machinery in this shop was of a very antiquated design. Most of the lathes had a chain feed. The machinery, I believe, for the most part, had been constructed right there in the shop.

Very soon after going to work for this company, I was given a job in the basement room on a slotting machine. The piece I was set to work on was a large forging intended for the crankshaft of a steamboat, and my job was to cut out of the solid forging the rough shape for the crank which was afterward to be finished in the lathe. The forging was so thick that it required the full stroke of the machine, which was an old and rickety one, and I was having lots of trouble in getting any work out of it. Mr. Holloway came down through the shop and stopped at my machine for a moment. He saw that I was having trouble and said, "Cox, you seem to be having trouble with the old slotter, but, never mind. Machines are like folks. You get along better with them after you are acquainted."

One of the big lathes in the lower story was standing idle for some time, owing to the illness of the operator. After I had finished the slotting out of the crankshaft, it was taken over to this lathe to be finished, and lay there on the floor for some days. One day as Mr. Holloway was making his round through the shop, I heard him say to the foreman that unless they could get that crank out pretty soon they would get behind on the job; whereupon I went up to Mr. Holloway and asked him if I could not run that lathe. He looked at me a minute and then said, "I don't know about that, young man. That is a pretty important job, and the man who runs that lathe is the only one that we feel is competent to do it," whereupon he walked off. I was a good deal crestfallen at this remark, but in the afternoon, having thought it over, he came back and put me on the job.

I started in to make a record for that lathe, and I succeeded so well that in a very short time I was notified by the men in the shop that I was going too fast, that the specified time for that crankshaft was a certain number of days. I did not pay any attention to the men, but went ahead all the more determined to see how quickly I could get the job out. I succeeded in cutting the time down from five to three days, and was complimented very highly by Mr. Holloway for the work. After that I had a good deal of trouble in that shop.

One day I went into the blacksmith shop to get a tool tempered for the planer. My job was running all right when I left the floor, but when I came back I found that someone had loosened one of the dogs that reverses the motion of the planer platen, and the platen had run out to its extreme limit and tipped up with one end on the floor. I knew what it meant but said nothing and got my machine running again as quickly as possible. My tools would not do any work, and it was only by standing right over the blacksmith and insisting upon having it done as I wanted it, that I could succeed in getting tools that would cut at all. The ill will of the men was confined to a comparatively few who had been born and brought up in Europe. There were some younger men who were glad to see the position I had taken. Two of them afterwards became leading engineers on the lakes.

It was not long after this that a party of gentlemen came into the works with some steel plates which they wanted to have drilled. One of these gentlemen, I remember distinctly, was Gen. James Barnett, and I learned afterward that they were a committee of the Board of Directors of the First National Bank, who were having a new safe or vault built. They came to see if the plates of which it was to be constructed met their requirements. Mr. Holloway turned me over to this committee to make the necessary tests in the drill press. I could not drill this plate with the ordinary drills the company had in stock. However, I told the gentlemen that I could make a drill that would do it. They told me to go ahead, and so I did. I got a first-class piece of tool steel from the blacksmith, had him make a short, stubbed, diamond pointed drill and then had him harden it very hard. I then put this drill in the biggest drill press in the shop and ran it at a very low speed and succeeded in perforating their test plate. I had observed in my visits to Billy Urquhart that they were able to turn chilled rolls by using a very hard tool and running the machine very slowly. I applied this principle to the drill press and succeeded. What the outcome of the test was, I never heard, but I flattered myself that they would have to bring me a harder piece than the one they had if they did not want it perforated.

The principal work on hand at the Cuyahoga Furnace shops when I was there was the building of a set of compound condensing engines for the first twin screw steamer ever built on the Great Lakes. She was a big wooden steamer with two keels and an engine over each keel.

The Amazon was not only the first twin screw steamer on the lakes, but was, I am convinced, the first one to be fitted with compound condensing engines. I remember reading a good deal about compound engines in Van Nostrand's Magazine about this time, and there was a wide difference of opinion among engineers as to their efficiency. I know these engines were built from new drawings and that Mr. Holloway spent a great part of his time in the drafting room and gave their construction careful personal attention.

I was given the job of planing out the bed plates for the engines to receive the caps that went over the main bearings. These bed plates were so large that they could not be put onto any planer in the shop. We not only could not get these big castings onto the planer, but we could not get them into a position where they could be put onto it. So I pursued something of the same policy that I had previously used in the mill for the four-foot pulley. I had the laborers move these big castings along on the floor of the shop until they were close to the end of the biggest planer. I leveled and squared them up. Then by means of a heavy timber, one end of which was put against the floor above and the other end on the top of a powerful jack screw, I clamped and fastened them firmly in place on the floor of the shop. Next, I took the cross head off the planer, fastened it to heavy angle irons on the end of the platen, and used this big planer with a platen some twenty feet long like a huge shaper with the tool traveling out and back.

Another job that was given to me was to bore out the hole in the propeller to fit the shaft. This propeller was very large; so large, in fact, that we could not get it into the machine shop at all; it therefore had to be done by hand. I blocked it up out in the yard, got it level, bored out two pieces of iron with a hole about two inches in diameter. Next I clamped these pieces over the hole in the propeller. After lining them up exactly, I put a bar through these two pieces with a slot in it for a tool, and rigged up a clamp with a screw, the point of which fitted the center hole in the bar. I then got four laborers to clamp some pieces of timber to this bar, and walked them round and round the wheel while I fed the bar through by hand.

When the engine was being erected in the steamer and the big crankshaft was lowered into the hold, the bed plates having previously been firmly secured, it was found that someone had made a mistake, as the crankshaft would not go into its proper place within $\frac{5}{8}$ of an inch. As I had turned the crankshaft the blame was laid on me, the foreman and all of the men uniting in that charge. I was very much upset by this circumstance, but nothing was said to me about it by Mr. Holloway at that time. I learned years afterward that on investigation Mr. Holloway found that one of the foreigners mentioned above, had purposely altered the drawing for the bed plate so that the man who fitted the bed plate worked to one set of figures, while I on the lathe turned the crankshaft to another set, with the result that the two did not fit together.

After the Cleveland Iron Company mill was rebuilt, I went back there to work, all the better for the experience I had gained in the Cuyahoga Furnace shops. By this time, Edmondson, the roll turner, had been made general superintendent of the mill, and as they needed help on the roll lathe, I went to work for Billy Urquhart. The roll lathe had been taken out of its previous corner in the machine shop and put over into a nice light shop immediately on the river bank. Not long after I went to work on the roll lathes, Billy Urquhart left the mill, for what reason I have forgotten, and a Welshman by the name of John Edwards was put in charge of the roll turning shops. We had to turn rolls for rails, for the puddling mill, for the bar mill, for the nine-inch guide mill, and for the eight-inch guide mill. These rolls varied in size from twenty-five inches in diameter, weighing three tons, down to the little eight-inch rolls weighing perhaps two hundred and fifty pounds. The labor in changing the lathe, which meant taking out one roll and putting in another, was often very great and sometimes it would take the biggest part of a day to get one big roll out and another one in. Edwards was lazy and spent very little time in the roll turning shop, putting the greater bulk of the work on me.

One hot summer day, when I was on the big work, I had just finished changing my lathe. Edwards, who had been allowing his lathe to run pretending to be busy, when I knew he was just nursing the job till I got through, turned to me and said, "Cox, now change my lathe. I have got to go up town." This made me mad, for I knew he had been planning the whole thing for the greater part of the afternoon. I replied, "I will be hanged if I will. I will quit first." To which he said, "Quit then if you want to." I washed up, rolled up my overalls, and went home. That evening, after thinking it over, I decided that I had made a mistake. The next morning I went to Mr. Ingersoll, told him the circumstances and said that I had made a fool of myself. I added if he would take me back I would go to work. Mr. Ingersoll smiled and said he guessed there would not be any trouble about it if I went back to work, which I did.

I worked steadily at the roll turning for two or three years. I soon got to be an expert at that class of work and received the highest wages paid to any mechanic about the mill at that time. This was $3.00 a day. I turned all the rolls used in the mill, roughing and finishing, rolls for rails, hand rounds, flats and guide rounds; also rolls for rolling plates. The grinding of the tools for chilled work was a delicate job and required a great deal of skill with the crude appliances provided for the purpose. My experience gained at this work enabled me a few years later to design and build for the Otis Steel Works a machine for accurately grinding the tools for turning plate mill rolls. This was the first machine of its kind, so far as I know, that was ever built.

During the summer of 1873 the Cleveland Iron Company leased a mill on the east side of the Cleveland, Columbus & Cincinnati Railroad tracks, called the Riverside Mill. I was sent over there to dress all the old rolls that had been lying in the mill unused for some years. I only mention this to show that at this time I was considered competent to take charge of an independent roll turning job.

While working on this job, there was erected, in the yard near me, a large plant for creosoting paving blocks for Nicholson pavement. I believe this was one of the first plants erected in the country for this purpose.

In turning rolls, especially for what we called a three high train, it was customary to finish completely the bottom roll first. The top and bottom rolls were very much larger in their external diameter than the middle roll, as these two rolls had on them the collars which fitted into recesses in the middle roll. After the bottom roll was completed, the middle roll was put into the lathe, the housings of the lathe being arranged to receive on top of the roll, which was being worked upon, the lower finished one. As the work progressed on the roll in the lathe, the recesses were one after another widened and deepened until the collars of the roll on top of it settled gradually into their places, the roll in the lathe driving by friction the one resting on top of it.

As these rolls were very heavy, averaging about three tons apiece, it was quite an undertaking to get the finished roll into the lathe. This was done by rolling the roll up on planks until it was in place and then gradually lowering it down onto the lathe housings. I was at work at this job one day and had the roll ready to lower into position. This was done by wedging the roll up in the middle, balancing it so that we could remove the planks from one end. Then by tilting the roll first one way and then the other, gradually remove the blocks and lower it down into place. That day I had one of these big rolls in this position, nicely balanced on the center-wedge, when a gang of mill men passed us. I was standing at one end of the roll to tilt it so that the men who were helping me could remove some of the planking from the end where I was standing. This gang of men saw that I was getting ready to lift on the end of the roll and they stopped and jeered at me. They knew the weight of the roll, but they did not know how I had it arranged. One of the fellows called out, that he bet I could not budge it. At that I bet him that I could. Without much difficulty, I tilted the roll so that one end came up about one inch, the fellows looking on in aston-ishment. I then bet this big fellow that he could not lift the other end. He stepped up to lift it, saying that if I could lift one end he knew he could lift the other. Just as he got ready to put his strength onto the roll, I slipped a wedge under my end of the roll with the toe of one foot. Of course, it was impossible for him to stir the heavy weight, and he went away a very astonished man with great respect for my physical ability. I have laughed over this incident many times as an example of the power of the mind over matter.

For my birthday present on my twenty-first birthday, May 15, 1873, mother sent me the gold watch which father carried with him during the war. She had this motto engraved on the inside cover, "Spes et Patientia," along with my name and the date.

In this connection a little history of this watch may be interesting. Uncle Theodore Cox was on father's staff and brought this watch with him from New York. Father at that time was carrying a very much cheaper open-faced watch. Uncle Theodore said it did not look well for him to be carrying a gold hunting case watch while the general carried a cheap one, so a trade was made, father giving Uncle Theodore a sword in addition. When father came home from the army, mother was carrying a large open-faced English watch which Grandfather Finney had bought in London and given to her, so another trade was made, father taking the large English watch and giving mother the smaller gold one. This is the one she afterwards gave to me for my birthday present. I carried this watch until 1897, when Mr. F. F. Prentiss bought for me at the factory of Patek Philippe & Co., Geneva, a little open-faced watch, which I now carry. I had new works put into the old watch, fitted it as a stem winder, and gave it to my son, Jacob, on his twenty-first birthday.

In the summer of 1874, while I was working in the mill, mother spent a few weeks at Niagara Falls, and I joined her there for a short vacation.

The boys used to go swimming regularly in Niagara River, just above the whirlpool. There was a little dock on the American side of the river that had at one time been used by the steamer "Maid of the Mist." Just above the dock there was an eddy, and what current there was would flow up stream. We boys used to go along the top of the cliff to a pine tree which grew up close to the bluff. We could reach the branches from the ground above and would climb down this tree to the swimming hole. I wish to say here that this is a fact and that several of us boys went in swimming regularly at that place. In relating this fact several times during my life, I have been regarded as a monumental liar, but it is a fact nevertheless.

At some time during my apprenticeship in the machine shop of the Cleveland Iron Company, I received what the men at the time called my "trade mark." I was grinding a planer tool on a badly worn out and cracked grindstone. The point of the tool caught in the crack of the grindstone and carried my left hand down into the frame of the machine, pinching off the ends of two of my fingers. This made it impossible for me to work for some time and those days of idleness I spent at Oberlin. Aunt Angie was visiting at grandfather's at the time, and every day she and I used to go over to the chemical laboratory to attend the lectures on physics by Dr. Dascomb. In the class was Dr. Dudley P. Allen, who was later regarded as the best surgeon in this part of the country.

I have still another "trade mark" evidence of my apprenticeship as a vise hand. Before I had become skillful with the hand hammer and chisel, I quite frequently used to miss the top of the chisel, the hammer hitting the thumb of my left hand. This was repeated at such frequent intervals that it produced a permanent red spot on my thumb.

Early in December, 1874, I concluded that I had acquired about all the experience in the mechanical department of the mill that I was likely to get. While talking to Harlo Hiems one day about my future plans, he advised me to learn the puddling trade and introduced me to John McCusker, who was considered the best puddler in the mill. He was a typical Irishman, short legs and huge body, and homely as a mud fence, but one of the kindest hearted men I ever met. After a short talk with McCusker, he agreed to take me on as an additional helper and teach me all he could of the art of boiling or puddling iron. As the puddling furnaces were run double turn, that is, day and night shifts, and as the day shift began work about four o'clock in the morning, it became necessary for me to change my boarding place. I therefore gave up my room at Mrs. Hapgood's and took a room at John McCusker's house. He lived in a little one-story cottage at the top of Columbus Street hill. There were only three rooms in the house, a front parlor or sitting room, a bedroom for John and his wife, and a dining room. The kitchen was a little "lean to" in the rear of the house. They put a bed in the front parlor for me, and as it was otherwise nicely but plainly furnished, I was very comfortably fixed.

Mrs. McCusker was a fine type of Irish woman, who had been for many years the housekeeper for Mrs. Willard's Young Ladies School in Troy, New York. It was while working in the mills in Troy that John McCusker became acquainted with her and married her. She was a splendid housekeeper, a good cook, and took as much interest in me as though I had been her own boy. She did everything she could to make my stay most comfortable.

I worked with John McCusker steadily from December, 1874 to June 15, 1875. Since I was an extra man, I worked the first two months without pay. The puddlers were paid so much per ton for the finished iron produced at the furnaces, out of which they paid their helpers. After two or three months, McCusker discharged his helper and I took his place at the regular helper's wages.

One night General Barnett came down to the mill with a party of young people, and they spent considerable time at our furnace watching the boiling of the iron. I was very much embarrassed by the presence of the young ladies, but managed to do my part of the job all right.

Each puddler was obliged to keep his furnace in order and the custom was that the puddler who had worked nights the previous week had to come down on Sunday and repair the furnace. Frequently we had to put an entirely new roof on the furnace. To do this we took off the old roof, filled the furnace full of ashes or cinders, shaped the top of the bed of ashes as we wished the under side of the roof to be when in place, then built the roof of fire brick, using fire clay as mortar. When completed we shoveled out the ashes, cleaning the inside of the furnace, leaving it all ready for the fire which was to be lighted by the night watchman Sunday night. The day shift, as I have said, began work about four in the morning. Each furnace (and there were thirteen of them) was taken in rotation. There was from fifteen minutes to half an hour allowed between the starting up of each furnace, so that when the heats should be made "ready" the iron could go to the rolls continuously till every heat was taken out. Some weeks therefore we were obliged to commence work at four in the morning, and some weeks not till seven or eight. When we began the work at four in the morning, we were generally through with our day's work by or before two in the afternoon. Usually as soon as the furnace was through with the day's work, the night gang began, and in this way the furnaces were constantly kept hot. There was no interval between the knocking off of one shift and the commencement of the other.

One very hot day, in the summer of '75, I was exhausted with the heat and labor and had to call upon the foreman in the puddling department to help me out. I knocked off before we had finished the day's work, and it was with difficulty that I got home. I had to sit down and rest every few minutes on the way up Columbus Street hill. I took a good bath and went to bed and slept fourteen hours without waking. Apparently I was completely overworked and exhausted.

By June 15, John McCusker pronounced me a first-class puddler and said he thought I knew as much about that branch of the business as he could teach me, and he thought he knew as much about it as any man in the mill.

As the hot months were coming on and I had just had an experience of what such weather meant at that kind of work, I decided I had better try something else. I then commenced working for the roller, Billy Bonell, who was the roller on the nine-inch guide mill where they made all kinds of iron, round, flat and square, from two-inch hand round down to about $\frac{7}{16}$ inch guide rounds. The largest flat bars we made on this mill were about two inches by one inch. I was perfectly familiar with all of the operations at the rolls, as it was necessary to understand them perfectly in order to do the roll turning job, but what I wished to acquire was the necessary skill in handling the tongs and hot iron bars. I still lived with the McCuskers, as the hours of the mill hands were practically the same as those of the puddlers and I could not at any ordinary boarding house get my meals at such times as were necessary.

While I was at work as roller's helper, the mill was shut down for a time owing to a strike. Mr. Ingersoll had given up the position as general manager, and at this time Mr. C. W. Bingham was acting in that capacity. I received a note from him one day asking me to meet him up in the city at the up-town office. When I arrived there he told me that they were having trouble at the blast furnace, as the men there who operated the hoisting machinery were on a strike, and that it was absolutely necessary to keep the furnace running. If the furnace cooled off with the iron in it, it would be ruined. He asked me therefore if I would help them out by running the hoisting engine. This, of course, I was ready and glad to do.

The hoisting engine was a peculiar affair and was up at the top of the blast furnace. There was a large drum in the top of the elevator shaft around which was coiled the wire rope that drew up the car. On the shaft of this big drum was a pinion about one foot in diameter, and engaged in this pinion was a vertical rack, the end of which was fastened to the end of the piston rod of the engine. The cylinder of the engine was about ten feet long, and one stroke of the engine raised the platform the entire distance, about ninety feet. The valve which operated it was so arranged that when the lever was pushed past the center in one direction the piston was forced up, and by pulling the lever back past the center the other way the piston was reversed. As originally constructed, the valve was intended at a certain point to shut off not only the inlet, but also the exhaust, the intention being to confine the exhaust near the end of a stroke so as to reduce the shock when the elevator stopped either at the top or bottom. This valve leaked horribly and once or twice I came very near throwing the wheelbarrow through the roof.

After working here a day or two, I was very much astonished, when the elevator came up, to find that instead of a load of iron ore it had on it the superintendent of the mill along with several visitors. As the superintendent stepped off the car on to the platform he looked at me and said, "My God, Cox, are you running this engine?" I smiled and said I was. He said, "If I had known that I never would have come up here."

I had not been running this engine very long when John McCusker told me one evening on coming home that the strikers had been to see him and told him that unless I stopped running that engine I would get into trouble. I do not remember now how this news got to my brother Charlie, but the next day he appeared in Cleveland with two revolvers, one for me and one for him, and proposed that we hold the fort. I laughed at Charlie and persuaded him to go home, as I did not think we would have occasion to use the weapons. I continued to run the engine until the strike was ended and saved the furnace for the company. They never acknowledged my services in any way, not even so much as by saying, "Thank you." I have always thought that this was somewhat strange, as I was, in fact, not working for the company at this time in any capacity. When I went to work for McCusker in December 1874, I ceased to be an employee of the company, as the puddler's helpers were responsible to no one but the puddler. The same was true of the mill gang. They were hired and they were paid by the roller, and in this way their names did not appear on the mill payroll.

The work at the rolls was not without its peculiar dangers. My job was to catch the end of the hot iron bar with the tongs as the bar came through the rolls and start it straight onto the standing room or floor of the mill so that it would continue to run out straight until the other end of the bar left the rolls. At this point I had to catch the bar with the tongs, give it a quarter turn over, and "stick" it in the proper pass in the next pair of rolls. Sometimes the end of a bar which was being rolled would split or, if it was too cool, would bend quickly upon coming out of the rolls and this required a quick eye and an almost intuitive action on my part to catch such a bar and guide it out straight in the way it should go. One day a bar which had been coming through the rolls back and forth in the ordinary way was turned the wrong way by the man on the other side of the mill when he "stuck" it in the last pass. The result was that the bar shot up into the air with a sudden spiral turn, going completely around me, falling in a ring on the floor of which I was the center. For a few minutes this made my hair stand up, but nothing serious came of it.

In the small guide mills, right next to where I was working, a few days afterward a small bar of round iron about ⅜ inch in diameter, under similar conditions was missed by the young fellow who was "catching" on that mill, and the end of the bar went through the calf of his leg and burned its way out. This crippled him for life.

I worked for Bonell on the rolls from June 15 until September 15, 1875, and by that time could handle the tongs and the iron as well as any man in the mill. I am able to fix these dates from an entry in my old expense book, where I find I paid $5.00 for a keg of beer to pay my "footing," as it was called, to the rollers gang.

I was never called by my right name by any of the men in the mill. Most of them always addressed me as "Governor," but one tall fellow at the puddling rolls always addressed me as "Mr. Secretary."

I was now thoroughly familiar with every process in the rolling mill, and I felt that I was competent to fill any position, under the superintendent, that might be given me. I was also confident that I could in a good many places improve upon the methods prevailing in that mill at that time, with a corresponding saving of money to the owners. I went to Mr. Bingham and told him how many years I had been working for the company and the various positions I had filled satisfactorily and that I did not see what more I could learn. I also cited the fact that for nearly a year I had been working there without any expense to the company, to acquire additional information and experience which could be obtained in no other way. Mr. Bingham referred me to the secretary and treasurer, Mr. Gus Fuller, who was up at the main office at the corner of Water Street and Superior Street hill. I went up there and interviewed Mr. Fuller. After explaining to him what I wanted, Mr. Fuller smiled and said he thought I was altogether too young to be entrusted with the position of foreman or assistant to the superintendent, but said that if I would go into some other mills in the country and post myself on the processes used in other mills, he thought they might at some later day give me such a position as I wanted. I was not looking for this kind of advice and felt that my long years of hard work deserved better recognition. However, as there was nothing to do in Cleveland, I packed my things and went to Toledo, where father was living and had been since 1873, when he was made president of the Toledo, Wabash & Western Railroad.

As president of the road, father knew a good many men in the iron business in the west. There was a rolling mill in Springfield, Illinois, and another one in East St. Louis, both on the line of the Wabash. From them the railroad company purchased a good deal of material. Father suggested that I go out to both of these mills and see if I could get employment in one of them. I did not lose any time in looking for new work, as I find I went to Toledo on September 16 and that I was in Springfield on September 17. The whole iron industry at this time was very much depressed, and I found that the western mills were reducing their force of men as rapidly as possible and that they could not give me any encouragement. With this situation, I came back to Toledo to wait for something to turn up.

My experience so far had been exclusively a practical one, but in the evenings I read a good deal. Father subscribed for and sent to me quite early in my experience Van Nostrand's Eclectic Engineering Magazine, which subscription I had always kept up. I also secured a copy of Ray's Arithmetic, Haswell's Hand Book of Engineering, Truan's Work on Iron, (this was an English publication which went very fully into the details of the English practice in iron making), Silliman's Work on Chemistry, and Bourne's Hand Book of the Steam Engine. These books I read and studied in the evenings. I felt strongly the need of greater knowledge of mechanical drawing, and set to work at once to acquire it. I cleaned up one of the rooms on the third floor, bought some drawing materials, a triangle, a book on mechanical drawing called A Text Book of Geometric Drawing, another text book on practical bookkeeping, and spent the greater part of each day in this room working by myself. Some time previous to this father had made me a present of a little box of drawing instruments, which I have always kept in good order in my desk. On the box in father's handwriting is the date, July 8, 1871.

After acquiring a little facility in the handling of my drawing tools, I made a complete set of drawings for a puddling furnace, drawn to scale, with all the tools to go with it. I also drew an improved form of damper of my own design.

From one of the cuts in the English book referred to above, I made a full set of detail drawings of a machine for punching holes in the ends of iron rails. I sent these drawings to Mr. McCusker, as I thought he would be interested in them. He was so pleased with my drawings of the puddling furnace that he showed them to Mr. Bingham who inquired where he got them. When Mr. McCusker told him that I had made the drawings and sent them to him, he seemed very much surprised. He said to Mr. McCusker that he wished he had known that I was capable of doing that kind of work before I left Cleveland.

Later I made some drawings of an improvement in the method of holding the rolls in the rolling mill housings. These I also sent to Mr. McCusker, who took them to Mr. Bingham, and I never saw them afterward.

I kept at my bookkeeping, using the examples in the text book, working them out both in single and double entry, and devoted part of each day to copying editorials from the New York "Nation." My object in doing this was to improve my handwriting, and also to acquire greater facility in the use of language.

It was during the winter of 1875 and 1876 that a heavy

westerly wind prevailed for several successive days, and the waters of Lake Erie were driven eastward so that the Maumee River ran practically dry from shore to shore. A man with a pair of ordinary boots on could have walked from one bank to the other. Many people in Toledo went down to the riverside to see the unusual appearance of what was ordinarily a navigable stream for large vessels.

There was at this time in Toledo a large new steel tug called the Carrington. This tug had been anchored in mid-stream, and when the water was driven out of the river by the gale, the tug fell over and lay on her side in the mud. No attempt was made to right her, the owners evidently thinking that as the water came back the tug would float as usual. Whether she stuck in the mud or whether her owners had miscalculated her center of buoyancy, I do not know, but the fact is when the water came back she remained at the bottom of the river. As the return of the water was accompanied by a very low temperature, the river froze over, and I with many others skated all around her.

So far as I know, this is the only instance where the waters of this river were driven out by a windstorm.

PART III

FOUNDING A BUSINESS

𝒮OME time in the early part of 1876, a gentleman by the name of Brown, representing the Niagara Bridge Company of Buffalo, New York, came to Toledo to see the officials of the Wabash Railroad in regard to some bridge contracts which were about to be let. I first met Mr. Brown in the office of Col. Sterling, who was the purchasing agent for the railroad company. Learning from me that I had had a practical training in the rolling mill business, he suggested that possibly I might find something to do in their mills at Buffalo. With this thought in mind and with father's permission, I went to Buffalo to see what I could do. I was taken through the rolling mill, which was a small one, and led to believe that in a few days they might give me a position, so I took a room at the hotel and waited.

The Niagara Bridge Company was largely owned by a Mr. Pratt, who also had in the city a large hardware store, where he spent the most of his time. Mr. Brown, whom I had met in Toledo, was a sort of confidential clerk to Mr. Pratt.

I stayed in Buffalo two or three days, and during that time frequently went into Mr. Pratt's hardware store. One day while there Brown introduced me to C. C. Newton, saying that Mr. Newton was a mechanic and was manufacturing twist drills in Dunkirk. Newton was a very bright fellow and a good talker, so I became very much interested in him. After Newton went out, Brown said to me that Newton needed capital to carry on his business, and if I had a small sum to invest, he did not know of a better opportunity for a young man than to go in business with Newton.

After waiting some days at the hotel, Mr. Pratt sent for me. I went up there expecting that the long-looked-for opportunity to get into the rolling mill business had arrived. I was very much disappointed and disgusted when Mr. Pratt told me that they had no opening in the mill, but they could give me a position as traveling salesman with a liberal commission on all orders for bridges that I could secure for the company. I saw at once that this was a bid for the bridges for the Wabash Railroad and that Mr. Pratt thought that by offering me such a position he would be sure to get a large amount of the work from the Wabash Railroad. I telegraphed father from the hotel that evening just what I thought of the situation, and in the morning received a dispatch from him to come home at once, which I did. When I reached home I told father of my interview with C. C. Newton.

Twist drills were an unknown tool to me at that time, as I had never seen one in use in any of the shops where I had worked or visited. The advantages of such a tool appealed to me strongly, and I told father that I believed there was a big future in their manufacture, as there was only one establishment in the country, namely, the Morse Twist Drill Company of New Bedford, Massachusetts, which was then making them. Nothing came of this interview for several days so I took the subject up with father again one evening, and he gave me permission to go back to Dunkirk to see Mr. Newton's shop and find out how much money would be necessary to give us a start.

I went to Dunkirk and called on Mr. Newton, and was a good deal disappointed to find that he had no shop, but rented room and power in a machine shop in Dunkirk, where he had only one lathe and one milling machine which he was using. Mr. Newton was very enthusiastic over the future of the business, and I went with him to several shops in the town where they were using tools which he had made. Every one spoke of them in the highest praise. I found that the work was practically at a standstill, as Newton owed money, partly on his machines and partly for raw material. He could not, with the small facilities he then had, earn enough to live on and meet his expenses. I inquired of several of the business men in Dunkirk as to Newton's character and standing in the town, whereupon everyone gave him a good recommendation. After some negotiations, Newton finally agreed that if I would put up $2,000.00 in cash, he would admit me as an equal partner with him in the business. I went back to Toledo and reported to father what I had learned in Dunkirk. After considering the matter a day or two, father told me that it was a very risky undertaking for men as young as we were, and that he could not afford to give me that amount of money. He did tell me, however, that since I felt so confident of the future outlook of the business, he would lend me $2,000.00, taking my note at 7% interest.

I accepted this proposition and returned to Dunkirk. Articles of partnership, dated Dunkirk, New York, June 27, 1876, were drawn up. Newton in the meantime had prepared an inventory of his assets, copy of which follows:

1 Lathe, 6 ft. bed 15 in. swing	.$200.00
1 Tap cutting machine and patterns	300.00
1 Milling machine and grinder attached	700.00
Unfinished polishing machine	40.00
Set of Master Taps	50.00
Wire Pointing Tools	10.00

Drill Chuck $10.00

Mandrel for emery wheel 3.00

Mandrel for cutters 3.00

Miscellaneous tools in case, including three squares,
hammers, etc. 50.00

Cutters for drills and all other purposes 250.00

All stock on hand, drills, taps, etc. 250.00

Stubbs steel wire, cut and uncut 60.00

Cast steel 75.00

Furnace 6.00

Crucibles 3.00

Patterns and castings for new Milling Machines . 54.00

Desk, cases for tool chests, etc. 130.00

Goods at Centennial 100.00

Plates and Wood Cuts 25.00

	$2,319.00
Less 10%	231.90
	$2,087.10
Amount due on lathe and printing	153.75
	$1,933.35

I was aware of the fact that this inventory was very greatly exaggerated. In fact, most of the articles enumerated were worthless, but I was content to go ahead, nevertheless, and signed the partnership papers.

The lathe mentioned in the inventory, Newton had purchased second-hand after it had gone through a fire. The only other item in the inventory, aside from the roll top desk, that was of any value whatever, was the milling machine designed to cut small twist drills running in size from about $\frac{1}{16}$ inch to $\frac{5}{16}$ inch in diameter. The patterns for this machine and some castings were included in the inventory. I saw the necessity of having more of these small machines and began at once to construct them.

I was very much surprised and greatly disappointed to find shortly that Newton was not a good mechanic. He was an ingenious man and a keen observer with a very retentive memory, but was not in any sense of the word a practical mechanic. I soon learned that his position in the tool room of the Brooks Locomotive Works (where I had been given to understand he had filled a position as tool maker) was simply that of a tool keeper, his duties being to give out the various tools in the room to the mechanics throughout the works as they were applied for. All he did was take the checks and place them in the compartment from which the tools had been taken. Mr. Newton was unable to give me any assistance whatever in the construction of the new milling machines, so we made arrangements with the Durrell Machine Company, in whose shop our tools were located, to give us the use of one man and their planer. I did all the lathe work myself. We commenced the construction of three of these small machines and pushed them with such speed that they were completed by September.

I was convinced that Dunkirk was no place for us to carry on the business, and discussed with Newton many times the desirability of changing to some other city. Philadelphia, Pittsburgh, Buffalo, and Cleveland were considered in our discussions. We finally decided that Cleveland would be the best place for us to start our venture. In the first place, I was well acquainted with the principal hardware dealers in Cleveland, George Worthington & Company, and Wm. Bingham & Company, and also with some of the bankers.

Second, we believed that the shipping facilities to the west and southwest were better in Cleveland than in any of the other cities mentioned.

When the three machines were nearly completed, Newton went to Cleveland to look for a shop. I gave him a letter of introduction to John McCusker and one or two other men whom I knew in Cleveland. Mr. McCusker showed Newton a building which had just been erected on Columbus Street. This building and location pleased him, and we rented the lower floor at 23 Columbus Street. It had a twenty-five foot frontage on Columbus and was seventy-five feet deep. This room we rented, with power, for $45.00 a month from a man by the name of James Langhorn.

This machine was built in 1876, from original patterns used by Newton & Cox for first drill milling machine

Next we ordered a new lathe from P. P. Blaisdell of Worcester, Massachusetts, and a small drill press from the same people, and ordered them shipped to this address in Cleveland. We packed up our machinery, paid all our bills in Dunkirk, and departed for Cleveland on August 26, 1876. On August 31 we made our first deposit in the Commercial National Bank of Cleveland. This was our beginning in Cleveland.

In Dunkirk our attention had been devoted entirely to the completion of the milling machines, and we had not tried to do much in the way of business. Our entire sales for the three months that we were in Dunkirk after I joined Mr. Newton were $31.26.

Mr. Newton and I went to board with Mrs. Hapgood, who had a house at this time on Euclid Avenue, west of Bond (now East 6th) Street. We occupied with A. H. Van Gorder and Frank Aldrich a large room on the third floor of the house. This was really an attic room with small windows and was called by the other boarders the "dormitory."

After getting our machinery arranged and running, we began to devote our attention to the sale of tools. On September 23 I find this entry in our day book: "Drew from bank per check No. 7 for C. C. Newton's expenses to Pittsburgh, $20.00."

We brought with us from Dunkirk a young man whom we had employed there to help us in building the machinery. Immediately upon arriving at Cleveland, I employed a first-class mechanic by the name of Walter Williamson, who used to come over to play checkers at John McCusker's house when I lived with him. Thus, when we started in Cleveland, our entire working force consisted of two men beside Newton and myself.

During my many years' experience in the shops, I had had opportunities of testing the quality of various brands of steel used for tools, both foreign and American, and I was satisfied that the American manufacturers could furnish us just as good steel as any of the foreign brands. As we could expect more prompt deliveries from the American manufacturers, we decided that we would use nothing but American steel and adopted that made by Miller, Metcalf & Parkin of Pittsburgh.

In the fall of 1876 the political excitement over the election of President Hayes was very great, and the marching bands of voters were very much in evidence every evening. The various ward clubs vied with each other in getting up the most striking and picturesque uniforms. One night the Republicans had a grand rally and torchlight procession of all the marching clubs. The assembly was in the Public Square.

As I had become acquainted years before with Mr. George W. Stockley, who was at this time interested with Mr. Charles Brush in manufacturing telegraphic and electrical instruments, I was invited one evening to be present when they made their first public demonstration of the Brush arc light. A large lantern, similar to a locomotive headlight, was arranged in one of the rooms on the south side of the Public Square. In the headlight was one of the first of Brush's electric arc lights, and we amused ourselves, to the annoyance and astonishment of the crowds in the Square, by throwing the beam of this light on them.

I was urged by Mr. Stockley to make an investment in the stock of this company, which was called at that time The Cleveland Telegraph Supply Company, but afterwards became the famous Brush Electric Light Company. The original holders made immense sums of money but, as I had no funds to invest, I missed this rare opportunity.

As soon as we were ready to take orders, I wrote to Col. Sterling, purchasing agent of the Wabash Railroad, and also to Mr. Johann, the master mechanic, soliciting their business, and was very soon rewarded with numerous orders, principally for staybolt taps and reamers. In January, 1877 we received several fine orders from the railroad. One of these orders was for sixty-four taper reamers, varying in diameter from $\frac{1}{2}$ inch, the smallest, to $1\frac{1}{2}$ inch, the largest. We had no difficulty in turning these reamers with the new lathe we had purchased, but as some of them were very long, I saw at once that we had no machine with which we could mill the flutes. It took several days to do the lathe work, and during this time I was anxiously studying how to finish them. While turning this problem over in my mind, I suddenly remembered a machine I had seen in the loft of the Cuyahoga Steam Furnace Company. At the time I could not imagine what it had been used for, but it now occurred to me that this was an old milling machine and that it would probably do the job we had in hand.

I went over there and asked permission to look at the machine and found that it was just what we wanted. It was a milling machine of very old design, evidently intended to be used for cutting keyways in the ends of shafting. It had housings on it like a planer; the platen was about eighteen inches wide and five feet long. Evidently it had been too light for the heavy work at the Cuyahoga Steam Furnace Company, and had been abandoned years before, as there seemed to be no one about the place who knew anything about the machine. Mr. Holloway kindly had this machine put on a wagon and delivered to our shop. With this machine we milled the reamers for the Wabash Railroad. As late as 1905 it was still a very important part of the equipment of The Cleveland Twist Drill Company, and was used almost daily. Among some old papers I find the memorandum of agree-

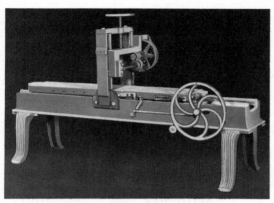

Early milling machine leased and later purchased from Cuyahoga Steam Furnace Company

ment made between the Cuyahoga Steam Furnace Company and Newton & Cox signed by Mr. Holloway and by C. C. Newton. By this agreement we were to keep the machine in good order and return it to the Cuyahoga Steam Furnace Company any time after five days' notice. Following is a copy of the agreement:

Memorandum of agreement by and between The Cuyahoga Steam Furnace Company and Newton & Cox, all of Cleveland, Ohio.

The Cuyahoga Steam Furnace Co. hereby lease to said Newton & Cox one Key Seat Milling Machine for the use of which Newton & Cox agree to keep the said machine in good running order, and to pay for the use of said machine the sum of Two Dollars per month from date until returned to said Cuyahoga Steam Furnace Co., and they further agree to return the above machine in good order within five days after receiving notice to do so from the above Cuyahoga Steam Furnace Co.

Cuyahoga Steam Furnace Co.
By L. F. Holloway, *Pres. & Supt.*
Newton & Cox,
May 11, 1877   By C. C. Newton

After using this machine a short time, we saw what a valuable one it was for us, so purchased it by delivering about $75.00 worth of twist drills to the Cuyahoga Steam Furnace Company and taking up the above contract.

The Cuyahoga Steam Furnace Company went out of existence many years ago, the plant having been sold to the Cleveland Ship Building Company.

The Cleveland Twist Drill Company would have great difficulty today (1905) in replacing this machine with anything which would be as well adapted to some of the peculiar work which they have to do, as this old one resurrected from the scrap heap, so to speak, in 1876.

Other good orders were received from the Wabash Railroad so that by March 1 they owed us by our ledger $585.99. We felt the necessity for more machinery, and in January or February ordered two more lathes, six foot bed, fourteen inch swing from P. Blaisdell & Company, Worcester, Massachusetts. One day these lathes arrived in the city. As Newton & Cox had no commercial rating in Dun & Bradstreet, Blaisdell & Company had forwarded the lathes and sent the bill through the express company, C. O. D. I was very much disturbed by this action of Blaisdell & Company and was debating with the teamster in the rear of the shop, trying to get him to deliver the lathes to us without the money, as we had not sufficient funds in the bank to meet the bill, when the postman came in at the front end of the building and left some mail on my desk. I left the teamster for a few moments and went into the office to open the mail, and much to my surprise and relief found a check from the Wabash Railroad for their bill in full. This gave us the means to pay for the two lathes. It was an exceedingly close shave for the new firm.

The milling machines which we had built to Mr. Newton's design in Dunkirk were very inefficient. The mechanism which he had designed for the twisting of the drill under the cutter was not only poorly designed, but was, in my judgment, contrary to good mechanical principles, as it required almost the entire power of the machine to feed the table forward and backward. When a $\frac{5}{16}$ inch drill was inserted in the chuck of these machines, I could, by grasping the drill with my thumb and finger, stop the machine. As I spent most of my time during the day on the milling machine, this defect grew on me to such an extent that it worried me. One evening after we had washed up to go home, I got to thinking of these machines and, with a piece of charcoal, sketched out on the floor of the shop an idea for their improvement. The next day I showed this sketch to Newton and explained to him the difficulty I was having and what I hoped to gain by the change. As a result of this conference I was given carte blanche to go ahead and make such changes as I thought proper. It only took a few days to accomplish what I desired, and the difference in the amount of work which the machine would do per day after the alterations were made was some-

574
62
16

HD9710
N57
K55
1986

38,47629Z
C361

TL33

C592

629209
L585

hines have been running daily
5 one of them was still at work
f The Cleveland Twist Drill
or special work on such orders
ke it pay to set up one of our

nd   ready to run the new lathes,
ssible for a workman to run
ecause he was very apt to
attending to the other. I
e lathes an automatic stop
nt addition, and since we
t, I made drawings of the
them, which were used
same job. Only within
een able to buy lathes
omatic stop feed incor-
such as we have been
the country, the stop
well designed for the
ur lathes in 1877.
y much embarrassed
point where it was
pay the few hands
turday afternoon I
rrow more money,
re in. Father said
it   absolutely neces-
reached that point yet.
was a bad plan for us to get into the habit of
borrowing money every time we felt a little pinched and that,

if I found after getting back to Cleveland that I must have more money, I could draw on him for such a sum as was necessary to tide us over the difficulty. I felt a little hurt at this, but at the same time could not but believe his advice was sound.

In the mill where I had worked so many years the custom had always been to pay about the 15th of the month, wages and salaries earned during the previous month. This was necessary in an institution as large as the rolling mill, where there were many hundreds of men employed, whose wages had to be figured per ton of output. This delay in pay gave the bookkeepers and timekeepers sufficient time after the closing of the month's business to figure out the payroll. I knew that most of the men working in Cleveland were accustomed to this method of payment. I therefore reluctantly announced on returning to the factory that hereafter Newton & Cox would pay in this manner. This left us a full two weeks longer in which to accumulate funds enough to pay the men the amounts due, and we got along without borrowing any more money at that time.

Early in the summer of 1877 Newton was married.

I find a memorandum of agreement written in our journal or day book, dated May, 1877, that the partners in the business could draw money for their personal use from that date, not to exceed $30.00 per month.

Father always gave me good advice. I do not remember whether it was at this time when I asked father to lend us money or at some previous time, but the motto which he gave me and which I always remembered through my business career was, "Go slow and learn to paddle." I have often thought of this saying of father's in our later and more prosperous years and have felt the wisdom of it, for in the early days we made many mistakes. I have said many times of late, that if we had had $50,000 to invest in business at the start, we probably would have ended in financial ruin. As it was, a good many of our early investments were mistakes, and it was only by going slow and learning to paddle, that we learned what we needed to know and how to handle the business. As our capital was very small, our mistakes were necessarily small in proportion.

With the one milling machine brought from Dunkirk and the three little ones we built, we could cut twist drills from $1\frac{1}{4}$ inch in diameter down to $\frac{1}{16}$ inch. It wasn't long until we felt very much the need for a machine capable of milling

This machine was built in 1877 to mill flutes on drills from $\frac{1}{2}$ inch to 5 inches in diameter

the flutes in drills larger than $1\frac{1}{4}$ inch. I therefore made a set of drawings for a milling machine substantially on the lines of what is known as the Lincoln Pattern, but the platen was arranged so that it could be swung on a center pin either to the right or left and the head arranged to impart to the drill the desired spiral motion. We hired a good mechanic by the name of John Malpas, whom I had met when working in the mill, and he devoted all of his time to the construction of this machine. It was a remarkably successful machine and has been in constant use in our factory ever since, and as late as 1905 it was still giving good service. With this machine we could mill either a right or left hand spiral, and could cut the flutes in drills as large as five inches in diameter. A short time after this machine was completed, Mr. Tabor from the Morse Twist Drill Company of New Bedford, Massachusetts, surprised me one day by calling on me. He told me that he had positive information that we were operating with machines that were a direct infringement of their patents and demanded admission to the factory for the purpose of satisfying himself whether or not his information was correct. I politely but firmly denied him permission, whereupon he went away and said he would return later with authority from the court to inspect our machinery.

I was very much disturbed by this, and that evening called at the house of Judge S. B. Prentiss. I related the circumstances to the judge and asked him if it was possible for Mr. Tabor to procure an order from the court to inspect an alleged infringement of patent. He said that Mr. Tabor could not do anything of the kind, and we never heard anything more on this subject.

Milling machines were very little used in this section of the country in 1878, and their advantages were not generally appreciated. As we were carrying on a new and interesting line of work in our shop, we were frequently visited by mechanics from various parts of the country. When they saw what our machines would do they were surprised, and we were often asked to build machines similar to those we were using. Thus, quite early in the history of the business we were manufacturing milling machines to sell. I made all the drawings both for the machines which we built for our own use and for those which we sold—the latter invariably being different in many details.

On October 9, 1878, I was married to Ellen Atwood Prentiss, the oldest daughter of Judge S. B. Prentiss. We were married very quietly at the home of Judge Prentiss, and instead of taking a wedding trip, I left the next day for a

Judge and Mrs. S. B. Prentiss, their daughters, Frank Prentiss, and young Houghton Cox

short business trip through the manufacturing towns of northeastern Ohio. Brother Charlie, who came down to the wedding, kindly volunteered to stay at the office a day or two to look after things while I was gone. When I returned we made our home with the old folks till we went to house-keeping early in 1882.

During this year the Cleveland Iron Company went into bankruptcy. The depression in the iron industry had continued and as a result they were unable to keep on with their enterprise. Their debts amounted at this time to $400,000.00.

In 1879 our little shop proved to be too small for the growing needs of the business. Mr. H. M. Hempy had just completed a new three-story building fifty feet front on West Street and seventy-five feet deep. This building was located in the rear of his planing mill. We rented the building at an annual charge of $900.00 a year, which included power. We had a very neat office fitted up on the lower floor with a separate room for making and caring for our drawings. Up until this time I not only had worked every day all day in the shop running machines, tempering tools, packing and shipping them, but had kept all the books and done all the correspondence. As my time now was being taken up more and more with making drawings for machinery, we engaged a young man as bookkeeper by the name of Fred Noltie. This relieved me of a lot of the bookkeeping.

Soon after moving into this new building, I went to a sign painter to get a sign to go on top of the building. In looking around he showed me the old sign of the Cleveland Iron Company lying in the yard back of his shop. This was just the right size for what I wanted, so I purchased the old Cleveland Iron Company's sign, had their name painted out and replaced by Newton & Cox. It struck me at the time as a rather unusual occurrence and the old motto "By this sign we conquer" flitted through my mind.

The lower floor of this building was devoted to the office and drafting room and to what we called our "machine shop." Here we had such machinery as was used in building machines for our own use and for sale. In the rear were the furnaces for tempering the tools.

The second floor was devoted to the lathes for turning twist drills, while on the third floor were the milling machines for milling twist drills, and a pattern shop. By this time we had work enough so that it was necessary to employ our own pattern maker.

Newton's taste ran towards the building of machinery to sell, and he devoted most of his time to securing orders for such machinery and neglected in great measure the business which we had originally started out to do, namely, the manufacturing of twist drills. Newton would take orders for machines which we had never built and for which we did not have drawings or patterns. He would send in these orders with his promise of delivery and put it up to me to get out the work. My time therefore was so much taken up with the designing and building of machinery for sale, that I also was obliged at this time to neglect the drill business.

We built in 1879 quite a number of planers ranging in size from 24 inches wide by 5 feet long to 36 inches wide by 8 feet long. I spent a great deal of time on the designing and drawing of these machines and invented a mechanism for shifting the belts of such machinery so that it was possible to drive the platen of the planer backward at a very much greater speed than was practicable to use for the forward or cutting motion. This was, so far as I know, the first invention in this direction. As we did not have money to spend for patent papers, we filed in April, 1880 a "caveat" protecting us temporarily in the use of this device. We have at the

One of many planers built by Newton & Cox in 1879

present time (1905) in the machine shop of The Cleveland Twist Drill Company, one of the 30 inch by 8 foot bed planers designed and built by me in 1879. It has been in constant use in our factory every day since it was built and has been recently pronounced by able mechanics, as twenty years in advance of the general design of such machines at the time it was built.

During this year I made sketches for a milling machine arranged to mill wagon axles complete in one revolution of the axle. I showed the sketches to the master mechanic of the Cleveland Axle Manufacturing Company, explaining to him what I expected to accomplish by the use of this machine and the saving it would be to their company to make axles in this way. He immediately gave me an order for the machine, which was a great success. But the master mechanic of the axle company applied for and secured a patent on this machine while I was busy constructing it. Afterward they built a great number of these machines for their own use.

During the summer of 1879, as in each previous summer for some years, I suffered from hay fever. My wife and Mrs. Prentiss insisted that I should try going to the seashore for a short time to see if I could get relief. I agreed and we went to Nantucket, where we spent the month of July. I was entirely free from hay fever while at Nantucket, but after we left there to come home, it came back on me with redoubled force. At Rochester I was in such bad condition that my wife and I left the train and went to the hotel to spend the night, the dust and heat in the train being unbearable. This convinced me that it would be necessary for me to get away from Cleveland during the summer months.

Meanwhile, Newton and I were not getting on at all well. He was of very little help to the business, yet was continually quarreling and finding fault. The situation grew worse and worse, and I finally got so I could not sleep nights worrying about it. Several times after lying awake most of the night, I would get up early in the morning, go down to the foot of Erie Street, get a rowboat and take a brisk row before breakfast. My wife knew what the trouble was, but I had counseled her to keep it from her father and mother as I did not want them to be disturbed by the situation. But, try as we might, we could not keep it from the old people. One day Judge Prentiss said to me that he knew something was wrong and asked me to tell him what the trouble was. I did so, and asked his advice as to what was the best thing to do under the circumstances. He said there was only one thing in his judgment to do, and that was to dissolve the partnership. He advised me to make an inventory of our business and to make Newton a proposition to buy or sell at a figure which I regarded as fair for half of the business. He added that he would lend me the money in case Newton should decide not to buy me out.

Early in June, 1880, unknown to Newton, I went thoroughly over the assets of the factory, appraised the machinery and made up a detailed inventory, which came to just $18,000.

One morning Newton came in and jumped on me about something that was going on in the shop. I concluded that this was the proper time to settle the question once and for all. I told him I had done business with him as long as I was going to and we had better settle the matter right now. Newton was very much surprised and asked me what I meant. I said, "I mean this. Our partnership has got to be dissolved. Here is an inventory of the business as it stands today. I will buy or sell for half of the amount of the inventory." After a moment's hesitation, Newton said, "I will buy you out if you will give me ten days to raise the money." Not wishing to take an unfair advantage of him, I said, "All right, I will give you ten days, but if at the end of that time you do not have the money, you must sell out to me." Newton turned on his heel and went out of the office.

He spent several days endeavoring to raise the money, going to Dunkirk and Buffalo, where he had many acquaintances. Evidently his friends had not as much confidence in him as he supposed they had, for he was forced to come back and accept my proposition.

PART IV

PROGRESS AND DISCOURAGEMENT

IN the early days of the business it was a part of the work of each man who tended a milling machine to back off the drills with a file. A man could very easily back clear, as we called it, more drills than he could mill on one machine. As we put in more machines, I found it more economical to have a man attend to as many machines as he could take care of and have the back clearing done by other men in a different part of the shop. This work increased so that we had eight or ten men at this time doing nothing but file the back clearance on drills. As they were all paid by the day and the work was tiresome, I felt that I was not getting as much work per man as I ought to have. I had introduced cards into the factory at this time on which each man entered the diameter of the drills and the number of each size which he back cleared per day.

The first step I took towards reducing the cost of this work was to charge up to each workman the files which he used on the job. I did this because I found that the men would not use the files after they became a little worn but throw them away and demand new ones. It was to stop this unnecessary waste that I introduced the practice of charging them with the files used. I kept careful count of the sizes and numbers each man turned out per day, and by changing the sizes from one man to another, in a short time I was able to estimate pretty closely how many drills of a given size the best man in the group could do. From this information I made up a schedule of piecework rates.

After completing my piece rate schedule, I submitted it to the men and asked them if they did not want to work on the piece plan. I told them that I believed they could earn more money on the schedule than we were able to pay them by the day. Everyone objected and did not want to do it. I did not feel in a position to force the matter, so let it drop for the time being.

A few days later a smart-looking little fellow came into the office and asked for work. I interviewed him and, as usual, asked him what he was accustomed to doing. He said, "I am a filer by trade." I asked him to explain what he meant by that. He said he was brought up in New England and had worked all his life in a gun shop and that his particular trade was the filing of the outer surface of gun barrels to make them round and smooth. I saw at once that this was the man I was looking for. I went upstairs and brought down a half dozen $1\frac{1}{4}$ inch drills, showed him what we wanted done in the back clearing of them, and asked him if he could do that job. He said that was just the kind of work he was accustomed to. I then produced my piece work list and asked him if he would undertake to do that kind of work on that basis of pay. After looking it over for a few moments, he said he would be glad to try it. The next day he started to work for us.

When he arrived, I took him up to the room where the other fellows were at work and laid out for him as much work as I thought he could do that day. In a few hours he came to me for more pieces, which I gave him. He continued to work right along and astonished me by the amount he could turn out. At the end of the week, when the men were paid off, he received several times as much money as any other man in that department. He did not show up the following Monday and I presume he went on a spree, for that was the last I ever saw of him, but the lesson was not lost.

The men in that department came to me the following Monday and wanted to know how it was that this stranger was paid so much more money than they. I told them that they had been working by the day and the other man had been working by the piece, and that he worked on the same schedule that I previously offered to them. Then they were all very anxious to go to work on a piecework basis. I gave them a revised schedule, and this was the beginning of the piecework system. Afterward I extended this system to all departments of the factory.

By this time I felt the necessity of having someone repre-

F. F. Prentiss, taken in as a partner on August 16, 1880

sent the business, traveling on the road soliciting orders. A cousin of my wife's, Mr. Francis F. Prentiss, had been in business for a year or more in Cleveland with an elderly gentleman, who had patented a brass padlock used largely in those days by railroad companies for locking switches so that they could not be moved by anyone unless he had a pass key. Mr. Prentiss was led to believe that this man had certain relations with the Pennsylvania Railroad, which would insure them large orders. He went into the business and worked at it hard and faithfully, but their locks were not a success and were rejected after several trials by the Pennsylvania Railroad, and the concern failed.

I had taken quite a fancy to Mr. Prentiss, who was much younger than myself, and in August, 1880, I offered to sell him a one-fourth interest in my business. After some negotiations, Mr. Prentiss' father came to Cleveland, and the partnership was finally closed on August 16. Mr. Prentiss was anxious to buy a one-half interest, but I had firmly made up my mind that I would not under any circumstances take in a partner owning as much of the business as I did, as I wished always to be in a position to control it myself. We finally compromised on a division of the interest whereby I sold Mr. Prentiss a two-fifths interest in the business for $8,000.00 —$3,000.00 of this was paid to me in cash and $5,000.00 in notes. The notes for $5,000.00 I turned over to Judge Prentiss to cancel that much of my debt to him. One thousand of the cash I paid to father and cancelled my debt to him. Father did not charge me any interest for the months of June and July. The balance I loaned to the firm from time to time to use as working capital, for which I took the firm's notes.

Shortly after Mr. Prentiss was admitted to the firm, I designed and built an automatic machine for pointing the ends of wire drill blanks. Blanks which had previously been cut off approximately all to the same length were placed in a hopper. The machine took the blanks from the hopper and carried them around where they were worked on both ends at the same time. Here, by suitably constructed knives, both ends were pointed exactly alike and to the proper shape of a drill point. Next they were automatically carried still further around and dropped into a box. After the machine was built I operated it for some time to satisfy myself that it was all right, and then had it taken up to the proper place in the shop to be used. The men had all kinds of trouble with this machine, and more than half the time it was standing idle. Shortly after this pointing machine was built, we engaged Mr. Lehman as superintendent. He formerly was employed in a similar capacity by the Bourne Nut & Bolt Works. As soon as Mr. Lehman became somewhat accustomed to his new duties in our shop, I explained to him the operations of this automatic machine. I told him that I had never been able to keep the men on it as they did not seem to understand it, but that I knew the machine was all right as I had run it myself. I explained to him that I wanted him to see if he couldn't keep it going. We never had any trouble at all with the machine after that, and as our business grew, we built more of them, and every one worked with perfect satisfaction.

As my duties were again growing and my time was taken up more and more with the study of "ways and means" to reduce production costs, I found that I could no longer do all of the drawing necessary. So in 1880 we engaged a young man, Charles O. Palmer, as mechanical draftsman.

When I went into partnership with Mr. Newton, I was entirely ignorant of all that pertained to the milling machine business, but as I grew more familiar with the manufacture of milling machines, I became convinced that the original machine built by Newton in Dunkirk was a copy of the machines and a direct infringement of the patents of Brown & Sharpe Manufacturing Company of Providence, Rhode Island. On the 24th of March, 1881, I wrote Brown & Sharpe on the subject, sending them a photograph of the milling machine in question, stating that I believed we were infringing their patent, but as we had built only one machine, we trusted they would forgive us. They wrote us under date of March 26, 1881, that we were infringing their patents, giving the claims which they had secured on that class of machines, and stating that they had recently licensed A. Alexander Pool of Newark, N. J., to make some machines like theirs at a royalty of $75.00 per machine. Also that they were willing to license us to do the same provided we paid that sum on those already built or made during the term of the patent.

I therefore sent our check to Brown & Sharpe for $75.00, and I firmly believe that by calling their attention to the matter we made a firm friend of this very important manufacturing establishment.

In 1881, or possibly as early as 1879, Mr. Graham of Galt, Canada, a blacksmith by trade, began to make twist drills by a forging process. He had a small shop and very limited means, and was unable to carry on the business successfully. In 1882 he wrote to us saying that he would like to sell us his patents, machinery and processes, and stating that if we purchased them, he would like to go to work for us to superintend the forging part of our business. I went to Galt to investigate his processes, and stayed there two or three days. I came to the conclusion that, while his forging process was

practical, it cost him more to get the forged drill into market-
able shape after the forging process was completed than it
cost us to make the goods complete from the raw material.

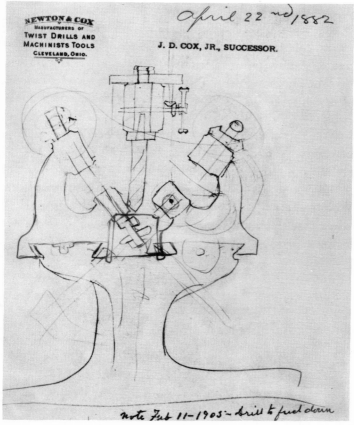

Pencil sketch of vertical duplex milling machine, 1882

After returning home, I wrote Mr. Graham that his proposition did not interest us.

In 1882 I invented a back clearing machine designed to give the body clearance on twist drills from ⅜ inch in diameter up to 1½ inch in diameter. This machine had two emery wheels, one for each flute. By suitable mechanism the wheels were moved longitudinally along the sides of the drills, back clearing both flutes at once. This machine was locked up in a room by itself and no one was allowed to see it, except the man operating it, until July, 1889, when I got a patent on it.

I find by a letter written to Francis Richards of Springfield, Massachusetts, July, 1882, stating that it cost us at that time $6.50 per hundred to back off ¾ inch drills. After the introduction of this machine, we cut the price down so that we were turning them out at 36 cents per hundred.

Up to this time we had been the only competitor of the Morse Twist Drill & Machine Company of New Bedford, Massachusetts. Some time during 1880, Mr. Babcock, a Morse Twist Drill Company salesman, came to Cleveland and got Mr. C. W. Bingham interested in the project of starting a twist drill company in Cleveland. On January 5, 1881, the company was incorporated, and they commenced building machinery in the second story of a building on the south side of Water Street hill. They were incorporated under the name of The Standard Tool Company, with an authorized capital stock of $100,000.00. This sum was nowhere near sufficient, and before they really became any factor in the market, they put into the business, by assessments on the stock, about $300,000.00. Several of the original stockholders became discouraged, but Mr. Bingham had faith in the final outcome of the business and purchased the stock of the dissatisfied stockholders.

This company, after working two or three years, moved into a three-story building on the southwest corner of Bond (now East 6th) and Rockwell Streets. They afterwards added a story to this building, making it four stories high. Later they bought land and built a factory on Central Avenue, near the Cleveland & Pittsburgh Railroad.

Until now we were milling all of our twist drills on machines which used but one cutter. I put in a great deal of time outside of business hours studying the problem of constructing a machine that would mill the two flutes in one operation. This I knew would cut in half the cost of milling the drills.

While deep in the study of this problem, I met quite by accident a Mr. Francis H. Richards, an inventor well known at that time in New England, who later became known all over the world as a genius in the building and constructing of complicated automatic machinery.

At the time that I met him he had just moved to Cleveland from Springfield, Massachusetts, so that he could secretly build an envelope manufacturing machine. He could not carry on this work in Springfield, which was in the center of the envelope industry, without having all of his movements watched and some of them anticipated. For this reason he had rented a room on the top floor of the Blackstone Block in this city and commenced the construction of what eventually proved to be a revolutionary machine in the envelope manufacturing business.

He became very much interested in our little factory, and I frequently talked with him about the many improvements which I felt we must inaugurate. One day he said he had an idea for a milling machine for our business which he thought would be a success. I tried several times to get him to make me a set of working drawings for such a machine, but his mind was so intensely occupied with the development of his envelope machine, that he could not concentrate on anything else.

After being here some time, he became ill and went back to his home in Springfield. While there I corresponded with him and got him to promise that as soon as he was well he would send me drawings for this milling machine. This correspondence was carried on during the months of April and May, 1882. On May 30, I wrote him to go ahead and have not only the drawings made in Springfield, but the patterns also. But Mr. Richards got interested in other things and nothing was done until June, when I went to Springfield determined to push the matter. I arrived on a Saturday afternoon, and went immediately to Mr. Richards' house and made an appointment with him for the next day. We went to his office right after breakfast Sunday morning, and he hurriedly sketched out on ordinary wrapping paper, without any measurements, his idea of a proper milling machine for our business.

I wrote Mr. Richards on June 30 as follows: "I returned home on Wednesday entirely used up with a heavy cold and am still suffering a good deal, though improving. I made drawings from four sheets of your sketches yesterday P.M. and laid in, in red ink, all the measurements and finished sizes, and they are now in the hands of the pattern maker. I enclose photograph of centering machine as you requested. I made the drawings for this machine just six years ago."

On July 19 I wrote Mr. Richards, "I shall have all of the castings in the shop for the drill machine tomorrow, and will let you know how we succeed."

The rough sketches which Mr. Richards gave me of a twist drill milling machine were merely suggestive. The details of the feeding mechanism, the spindles, and the manner of obtaining the taper web, were all worked out by myself after

I returned home. At the present time (1905) our factory is equipped with over a hundred of these machines and we can cut two flutes at a time on all sizes of twist drills from .015″ diameter up to three inches. I find that we can mill a three

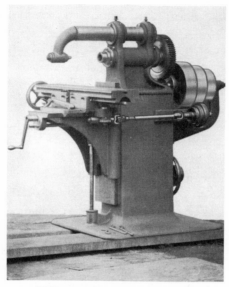

Milling machine, built about 1880

inch drill on one of these duplex milling machines in one hour and twenty minutes. Previously all drills larger than two inches were milled on the old Lincoln miller which I designed and built about 1877, and it required two hours and fifty minutes for one three inch drill.

I had felt for a long time that we were making a mistake in devoting so much of our time and capital to the manufacturing of machinery to sell. In order to satisfy myself fully as to the advisability of making any change, I had for a year or more kept close account of the cost of manufacturing machinery and the income from the same, as compared with the cost of manufacturing twist drills and the income from their sale. I satisfied myself that it would be greatly to our advantage to drop the manufacture of machinery and devote our entire attention to twist drills. Upon the return of Mr. Prentiss from one of his trips, I laid before him figures which showed that we were diverting the profits received from the manufacture of twist drills to the building of machinery, which did not yield us nearly so much profit for the capital and time invested. We therefore decided at once to abandon the manufacture of machinery.

When we announced this decision, a Mr. Eynon, who was the foreman in the machine shop, said he would like to buy our patterns and start in the machine business himself. The arrangement was soon completed and we sold to W. R. Eynon & Son all the patterns of the machinery which we were constructing to sell. We also sold them some of the machinery which we had bought for building these machines. The remainder of our large and heavy machinery, such as we did not now need for our own work, was sold to other parties, and with the money thus obtained we greatly increased our facilities for making twist drills.

One day in the summer of 1883, as I went into the milling machine room, I noticed that one of the operators was just about to pour the soda water from a large pail under his machine into the receptacle over the machine. This was common practice whereby the lubricant could run back over the cutters and down into the pail again. It struck me that this operation alone consumed a good deal of his time, so I waited about in the room until it was necessary for him to repeat the operation. In the meantime, I had noted by my watch how long it took the same man to take out of the machine a completed drill and put in a fresh blank. When he again changed the water on his machine, I timed him with my watch and found that it took longer to change the water than it did to change the blanks in the machine. I immediately figured out a system of pipes and tanks which, by means of a pump operated from the line shaft, could handle the water for the entire room. This was installed as rapidly as possible, and in a short time we were able to reduce materially the number of men required to run the milling machines. This system of supplying lubricant to milling machines has been favorably commented upon by many manufacturers who have seen it, and it has been adopted by many of them.

In 1884 father presented me with a microscope, and I spent much of my time evenings at home working with it. I became quite skillful in the handling and mounting of microscopic objects and did some creditable work in photographic enlargements of fly's heads, mosquito stings, and similar transparent objects. Father was president of the American Microscopical Society about this time, and I forged out of large needles a set of tools for him to use in trimming and finishing mounted photographic slides.

Business at this time was very bad. On November 8 I wrote to brother Charlie, who was on his cattle ranch near Denver:

"Business is terribly dull here. We are selling about one-third the amount of goods we ought to, and over one-half of our machinery has been idle for three months."

Here is a copy of a letter written by Mr. Prentiss to me August 13, 1884, which shows how he felt in regard to the business at this time:

Dear Dolson:

Yours of the 10th at hand. Here are the sales for June, July and August '83—$11,251.55, and for June and July '84—$4,224.06; for this month they may go to $1,800.00, making $6,024.06 for the same three months this year, or $5,000.00 less than last year. These cold figures are what convinces me we must do something immediately. It looks to me as though a Stock Company is the most advisable recourse. I don't go into it without misgivings, too, but if we don't have a Company, what are we to do? I realize that you and I would have to submit to a great deal of annoyance and worry from complaints and dissensions of stockholders; but I can stand all that better than I can running deeper and deeper into debt every month. This can be talked over when you return. In making arrangements for a Company the understanding could be that the Company pay, or rather assume, all our liabilities. We should expect to have $50,000.00 or $75,000.00 cash and Uncle Samuel's loan could be taken up as soon as the cash is paid in.

I have written Mr. Foot. Will see Charlie Baldwin in a few days.

Yours,
Frank.

At the same time Mr. Prentiss wrote to James D. Foot of New York City, who was our sales agent for the New England and eastern territory, as follows:

Aug. 13th, 1884

"We have about made up our minds to make a Stock Company of this concern. We shall complete arrangements within the next sixty days. We can't say what the capital will be, probably $150,000.00; whatever it is we shall hold little over one-half. If you want stock, let us know as soon as convenient."

On my return to Cleveland, I consulted Judge Baldwin about setting up a stock company. After asking me some questions about the business, he said he thought we had no

Jacob D. Cox, Sr., 1885

reason to feel discouraged and advised strongly against the stock company proposition. As I was never heartily in favor of the idea, the subject was dropped without any effort to secure subscribers for the stock.

During this year I made a complete set of sketches for an automatic drill milling machine, but as in many such cases, could not find the time to work out the details in the drafting room. Nothing was ever done with the sketches until 1892, when I turned the entire lot over to our machine shop foreman, Mr. Wm. T. Armstrong. After studying my sketches and after frequent consultations, he succeeded in building an automatic machine for milling ¼ inch twist drills. But it never did satisfactory work, and although three machines were built it was finally abandoned.

I find in my sketch book that on March 25, 1893, I suggested replacing the long levers used in this machine by a cam motion, which I now believe would have made the machine in every respect a success. But Armstrong was not familiar with this way of obtaining motion, and nothing was done with my suggestion.

Owing to the fact that business had been steadily declining for the past two years, on January 1, 1885, I felt forced to discharge Mr. Lehman, and by doing so saved his salary amounting to $1,200.00 a year. This very greatly increased the amount of detail work which I had to do, as I assumed his duties.

On February 1, I wrote to father: "I have been a very busy man since the first of January, as we have discharged our superintendent, and I have assumed his duties in addition to my own; consequently, I have found it impossible to write any but business letters and have to cut them as short as possible. I have been intending to give you a report of our business for 1884, knowing that you would be interested in it. I was very much afraid that we had at most only made our expenses, and to be sure that we should not overestimate our worth, we took 5% off our last inventory on all machinery and general plant account. Expecting a drop in the price of twist drills, we cut our stock on hand down 15% more than last year, inventorying it at 60% off the list; lowest selling price now, and for 1884, is 55%. Taking these items into

General Cox, Dean of the Cincinnati Law School, about 1885

account, I think we have no reason to feel discouraged in spite of the exceedingly dull times. I give you also some items of interest to show what it costs to run even a small business:

General expense . . . . $ 2,783.00
Labor wages 18,305.00
Transportation 392.00
Traveling expenses 1,158.00

Stationery	. . . .	$ 199.00
Postage	. . . .	314.00
Advertising	. . . .	692.00
Blacksmithing	. . . .	356.00
Collections	. . . .	83.00
Insurance .	. . . .	399.00
Discounts .	. . . .	189.00
Interest	. . . .	375.00
Royalty	. . . .	24.00
Steel	. . . .	9,050.00
Rent .	. . . .	899.00
		$35,218.00
Inventory January 1st, 1885	. . . . . .	$60,035.85
Bank credits .	. . . .	3,140.73
		$63,176.58
Liabilities	. . . .	17,043.25
Present worth	. . . .	$46,133.33
January 1st, 1884, worth	. . . . . .	40,668.61
Increase in one year	. . . .	$ 5,464.72

"I think after the first of February, business will slowly revive and that it will take probably two years to get back where we were in June of 1883, which was the best single month we ever had. (Sales for June, 1883, $4,097.97.)

"To give you some idea of the state of our business, I will say that our sales for January were only $1,200.00."

During the summer my health was so poor that I had to give up work for several weeks, which I spent at Ballast Island.

Some time during the year 1886 I took up for amusement and recreation the designing of yachts, and made several designs to scale. I photographed the drawings and sent them to father to show that I had reached considerable proficiency in this line of work. I happened to show one of these photographs to a boat builder in this city a short time after com-

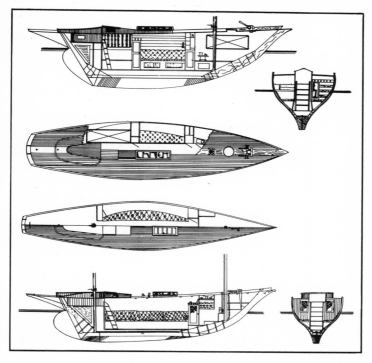

Sketches of yacht designed by Mr. Cox in 1886

pleting it, and he asked me if I would sell him the design. I told him I would not sell it to him, but if he wanted to build a boat from my design, he could have it. My impression now is that I gave him the entire set of original drawings. As he has built several yachts for the lakes since then, I have no doubt he has used my designs in some way.

During this summer I purchased a canoe. As we were near the river, I used to go directly from the factory Saturday noon and spend most of the afternoon paddling on the lake or up the river. This was good exercise, and partially filled the need of recreation.

This summer, too, I invented and built a back clearing machine for putting the body clearance on *small* drills. We did not have a good machine for this, and I had a standing offer that I would give $100.00 to any man in the shop who would get up a good machine for this purpose. We tried one or two suggestions made by the men, but they were failures. For a long time I had had this operation in my mind continuously without being able to see any light on it. One day as I was coming down Euclid Avenue, near the corner of Bond Street, without thinking particularly of this machine, an idea suddenly popped into my head, and I could see the finished machine as clearly as though I had a photograph of it. When I reached the factory, I proceeded at once, by means of blocks of wood and such other appliances as I could find around the factory, to try an experiment to satisfy myself whether or not the idea would work. I kept at that job all the afternoon, and by quitting time had thoroughly convinced myself that the machine would operate successfully. We went to work as quickly as possible and constructed a machine according to my idea. In a letter to father, dated January 22, 1887, I told him that a boy at 75 cents per day can do more work with this machine than six smart men by hand, at a saving to us of $14.25 per day.

We have built many of these machines since then, and at this writing (1905) they are still at work in the factory. We found as we needed more machines that we could enlarge them for heavier work, and finally built machines on this same plan large enough to back off 3 inch drills. It was a surprise to me to find that this style of machine, with only one emery wheel, would do more work in a day than the one I had originally designed with two emery wheels, both working at the same time. The increased output was made possible by the simplicity of the machine and the facility with which the pieces being operated on could be handled.

I also designed during this year an automatic tap chasing lathe, but this machine was never built as I was opposed to our

Judge Prentiss' house (left) and Mr. Cox's house on Euclid Avenue, 1886

company going into the manufacturing of taps on a large scale.

During this year The Standard Tool Company asked us what we would sell out to them for, and I replied to their letter on May 21, 1886, as follows:

"Complying with your request we submit below, proposition for the sale of our business; this proposition to be withdrawn at noon of the 25th of May if not accepted sooner.

"We will sell to you our entire business including machinery, fixtures, stock on hand of finished and unfinished goods, raw materials, etc., patents, goodwill and book accounts, for the sum of Seventy-five Thousand Dollars in cash down, or its equivalent."

Fortunately for us this offer was not accepted.

Shortly after this Mr. Prentiss and I made a trip east to see if the Morse Twist Drill Company at New Bedford could be interested in buying us out. But this trip was, fortunately, equally unproductive.

Our two larger and more powerful competitors having thus declined to buy us out, we had to go on as best we could. We were definitely on our own. But as it turned out, we were just at the beginning of our period of most rapid growth.

PART V

BROADENING THE FOUNDATION

IN 1887 I took out a patent on adjustable guides for drill blanks to be used on our drill milling machines.

By this time our volume of business had grown substantially and we found our factory too small for us. Our lease with Mr. Hempy was for a term of years and it took some ingenuity to get permission from him to throw up the lease, but we finally succeeded in doing this and began looking for another location. Some time previous to this Mr. Winthrop Ingersoll had purchased a half interest in Mr. William Eynon's business, which he had previously purchased from us. Eynon and Ingersoll also were looking for larger quarters. Mr. Prentiss and I looked at several places in the city that were for sale, among them a large brick block on Case Avenue (now East 40th St.), near Hough Avenue. I believe this building had originally been built for the Wilson Sewing Machine Company, but we thought it was too large for us to purchase at this time.

Mr. Ingersoll had also been looking around for a suitable location and finally came to us with a proposition, that if we would lease from them a building to be erected to suit us, they would purchase the lot 100 feet front on Lake Street at the corner of Kirtland (now East 49th Street). The property ran back 333 feet on Kirtland Street. They were to build a two-story building for themselves, in which were to be placed the boiler and engine. If we were agreeable, they would build for us a building 90 feet long and three stories high on the Lake Street side. The rental being fixed at what we regarded as a fair price, we closed the arrangements with them. Judge

Ingersoll then bought the lot and put up the buildings. A photograph of these buildings as originally erected may be of interest.

The Cleveland Twist Drill Company, in 1888, taken from corner of Lakeside Avenue and East 49th Street

This building was to be ready for us early in 1888, but through some delays the buildings were not completed until June.

Since we had a good deal of material and stock to move from the old factory to the new one, we decided to buy a horse and wagon so we could do a great deal of this ourselves. After looking at several horses and driving some of them myself, I finally bought from Mr. Ford, who kept a livery stable on Champlain Street, a young cream-colored horse and a light spring wagon. Billy Urquhart, who was now working for us, had a stable in the rear of his house and was quite pleased with the idea of taking care of the horse. For doing so he was to have the privilege of taking him home at night and driving him down in the morning. I drove the horse all about the city most of the day, taking him to the various railroad stations, and to me the horse seemed to be well broken and perfectly satisfactory in every way. He was strong and quick in his movement, and we thought we had a capital horse.

Billy Urquhart

Billy drove him home that night, but the next day did not get down to the factory until about ten o'clock in the morning. A madder man you never saw. He said I had bought the meanest horse he ever saw in his life, and he told me that the man did not live that could put a bridle on him. At my suggestion we both got in the wagon and drove to the livery stable where I complained to Mr. Ford that the horse had bad habits. He replied that they had never had any trouble with him. This seemed strange to me, so I asked him to take the horse out of the wagon, take his harness off and then let

me see them hitch him up. They would not do this without
some persuasion, but finally it was done. The minute they
tried to put the bridle on Dave, he threw his head straight
up into the air and held it there in spite of all they could do.
Finally one of the stable men got a stick with a loop of catgut

*The Cleveland Twist Drill Company's first delivery wagon.
Houghton Cox with back to camera; J. D. Cox, Jr., in center*

on the end. Then without any bridle in his hands and with the
stick behind him, he walked up to Dave, patted him and thus
easily succeeded in getting his hands on the horse's nose,
whereupon he twisted the catgut around his nose until the
horse fairly trembled with pain. Another man then brought
him the bridle and they succeeded in getting it on. After that
Dave was as meek as a lamb and they had no further trouble
in hitching him up.

We went back to the shop, but at noon when we came to
hitch the horse up again, had the same trouble. We simply
could not get the bridle anywhere near his head. A black-

smith in the neighborhood said he could put it on, and volunteered to try, but after repeated efforts, gave it up. We finally succeeded some way in getting him hitched up. I told Billy when he went home that night to leave the bridle on all night, then he would not have any trouble in the morning. I believe Billy did this for the next day or two, for he was on hand on time in the morning. A few days later he was again very late, and this time so discouraged that he wanted us to relieve him of the care of the horse.

I was very much amused but saw that something must be done to break the horse of this habit. I concluded that at some time he must have been whipped or abused and would throw his head up out of fear. I determined to cure him of this habit if possible, and had a good strong eye bolt made and screwed into the barn floor. I bought a strong rope halter and got a small pair of rope pulley blocks. These I gave to Billy and told him if the horse refused to take the bridle on the following morning, not to whip or abuse him, but hook in the block and tackle and pull his nose right down to the barn floor, then go away and leave him for some time. Later offer him the bridle again, and if he refused, repeat the operation until the horse gave up. My instructions were to keep at it if it took all day, and not to give the horse anything to eat until he took the bridle. Billy did just as I told him and had quite a protracted struggle with the animal, but in the afternoon came down to the factory smiling with triumph. He said that Dave took the bridle at last as meekly as a lamb. We never had any trouble with the horse in this regard afterwards.

Shortly after moving into the Kirtland Street factory the horse developed another bad habit. He would stand on the street hitched to the wagon by the hour without giving any trouble, but when we did not need him we used to drive him into a shed back of the factory and leave him there hitched to the wagon. He must have gotten tired of this for some reason or other, for he repeatedly kicked the dashboard out of the wagon when in the shed. It got so that we did not dare to drive him into the shed hitched to the wagon.

As it was inconvenient to take him out of the wagon every time he came into the yard, I determined to cure him of this habit. I got a piece of six inch square timber and arranged it with a hinge on one end so that as soon as the horse was driven into his place in the shed, I could lower this heavy timber and fasten it securely in place two or three inches above his hind quarters. After we had this appliance ready to use, we drove Dave into the shed, fastened the timber in place, and waited developments. The horse looked round several times to see where we were, so we got out of sight, but still where we could watch him. In a few minutes he tried to give a vigorous kick but was surprised to bump up against the heavy timber. After two or three trials, he saw he was beaten and gave it up. This cured him of kicking while in the barn, and after a time we removed the timber and never had any more trouble with him. We kept him for several years, until he got so lame from continual driving on the hard pavement, that the humane agent told our boy if he ever caught him down town again with that horse, he would arrest him. We had to sell him, but we never had as good a horse afterwards.

During the summer of 1889, while at the seashore, I became acquainted with Dr. W. M. Jameson, who was the owner of a pretty little 21-foot cutter called the "Bantam." I used to

go sailing with him nearly every day and got my first experience in handling a sailing yacht. The rig of this boat was a
little too large for one man to handle comfortably, and the
result was that Dr. Jameson never left his moorings without
me; and I became his right-hand man. We went often to
Marblehead and entered many of the Marblehead Yacht
Club races, but the doctor was always slow in getting 'round.
We never secured a good place at the start and never won a
race.

Employees of The Cleveland Twist Drill Company in 1889

In the summer of 1890, Mr. H. A. Garfield came to
Magnolia to spend the summer. I wanted very much to have
the pleasure of sailing with him, but I could not, of course,
invite him onto another man's boat, so I determined to buy
one of my own. Harry Garfield and I went down one morning
to Swampscott where they make a specialty of sailing dories.
We found there a fine sample of that style of boat about 18

feet long, decked over at both ends and along the sides. I bought this boat for $100.00 and took her to Magnolia, where we had great fun with her all summer.

"Nahma," my first boat—a sailing dory

The Ingersoll Milling Machine Company did not progress as well as they had hoped, and took up negotiations with several western towns for a new locatiom. Some of these towns were giving a bonus to manufacturing establishments to move west. They succeeded in making satisfactory arrangements, and announced to us that they were going to move to Rockford, Illinois. We had a long term lease with them for the use of the building and the power, with a provision in the lease, that if for any reason they should not furnish us power for more than three days at any one time, we would have the privilege of running the engine ourselves and deducting from the rental $1.00 per day. After consulting with Mr. W. C. Cochran, we found that this lease was as binding on us as on the Ingersoll Milling Machine Company, and that they could compel us to go on renting the building and furnishing our own power. We found that this would cost us from $3.00 to $5.00 per day. We therefore entered into negotiations with them for the purchase of the lot and buildings and finally closed the bargain with them. We paid Judge Ingersoll $19,000.00 on January 1, 1891, for the buildings as they stood, including engine, pulleys, pumps, and shafting.

Our business had grown steadily during these years, our sales having increased from $37,573.00 for the year 1883 to $80,853.00 for the year 1890. We needed more room for our tempering department, so during the year I made complete drawings for an addition to the Kirtland Street building which we had purchased from Ingersoll. We raised the building one story and added fifteen feet to the end of it. We also put in staircases and an elevator. As I had never made any architectural drawings, I was a little doubtful about the builders accepting them to work by. On opening negotiations with a builder, I showed him the drawings and specifications which I had drawn up and asked him if they would be satisfactory. He complimented me upon the work and said that I could not have done better if I had been an architect. This, of course, was very flattering. The drawings and specifications were followed and everything came out just as I wished it. We had now doubled our floor space.

When we bought the Ingersoll property, the lot had never been fenced in and the Pennsylvania Railroad had run a switch track across the rear of the lot in a curve so that they could run their cars from the tracks in the rear of this lot

Our summer home at Magnolia Point

View of the rocky seashore from our window

down Kirtland Street and connect with the Lake Shore track on the lake front. This was done prior to the purchase of the lot by Mr. Ingersoll. The constant passing of the switch engines and trains across our property and the consequent inability to fence in the lot was a source of great annoyance to us, so I opened negotiations with the Pennsylvania Railroad to remove their tracks. They were reluctant to move and finally came to us asking whether we would consider a fair remuneration, if they were to keep their tracks there permanently and acquire the right to do so. I told them the only consideration we would accept was the purchase by them, and deed to us, of the next lot west of us on Lake Street. They seriously considered this proposition and sent Mr. J. G. W. Cowles out to look at the property. His mission was also to get a price on it. The matter was delayed until I became disgusted and finally went to Harry Garfield and employed him as an attorney to compel the railroad company to move. We finally succeeded in getting them to do so in August, 1892.

I was very anxious to have father spend his summers with us at the seashore. We had been going regularly every summer for several years to Magnolia Point, where we had engaged rooms in a cottage. We had the same rooms year after year, and our children knew no other summer home. As an inducement to get father to go to the seashore, I bought a 21-foot cutter yacht, the "Cy-Pres," in the spring of 1891.

Father was an enthusiastic sailor and the idea of spending most of the summer on the water appealed to him. After father came I had the pleasure of sailing the "Cy-Pres" with him up and down the New England coast all that summer.

We had never had our books audited since starting the

"Cy-Pres"

business, and somehow I felt we ought to have this done so as to be sure that we knew just how we stood. In the fall of 1891 I engaged an expert, who came to the office and went thoroughly over our books. In December he gave us a statement which showed that we had $156,105.13 in assets, and that we owed, including payroll due the first of January, $43,376.01. This left us a net balance of $112,729.12. Most of the indebtedness of $43,376.01 was for money borrowed from time to time from my father and from Judge Prentiss.

In 1892, as our boys, Jacob and Houghton, were going to University School, I contributed $1,000.00 to the fund for their building and was elected a member of the corporation of the school. Soon after I was elected to the board of trustees.

Jacob D. Cox, Jr., at 11 years   *Houghton Cox, at 12 years*

The Board of Trade of Cleveland had been in existence for many years, but it had a very small membership, composed almost entirely of wholesale and commission men. They occupied rooms in the old Atwater Block in the flatiron shaped building between South Water Street and Superior Street hill. The Board confined itself entirely to questions relating to the commission and grain business and had very little, if any, influence on general business or civic questions.

Early in the year 1892 some of the younger business men of the city saw the necessity of a strong association that could take up all questions of general interest. Mr. George P. McIntosh was the prime mover in this matter and organized a "Committee on the Promotion of Industry." His intention was that this committee should consist of a hundred energetic business men. Each one was to contribute $20.00 annually for the expenses of the committee. I became a member of this committee.

It soon developed that there was an enormous amount of work to be done—more than the members could find time to do—so in August of this year correspondence was opened with Mr. Ryerson Ritchie, who was then the secretary of the Board of Trade of Kansas City. In November of this year Mr. Ritchie came to Cleveland as the secretary of the "Committee on the Promotion of Industry." Mr. Ritchie was a fine organizer, in love with this kind of work, and this committee soon became the leading business organization of the city.

In February, 1893, through the efforts of this committee, it was merged with the old Board of Trade, and the new organization was called The Cleveland Chamber of Commerce. In April, 1893, a new Board was elected by the Chamber of Commerce. In June the Chamber opened a handsome suite of rooms in The Arcade, where they continued to hold their meetings for a number of years. I was appointed chairman of the Membership Committee and worked hard on that committee for two years to bring the membership up to a thousand.

The business of The Cleveland Twist Drill Company had continued to grow rapidly, and judging from our rate of growth in the past two or three years, we felt that the time was not far distant when we would need more room. There was a vacant lot 100 feet front on Lake Street, immediately west of us between our property and that of the Cleveland Hardware Company, so we opened negotiations for the purchase of this lot. The Cleveland Hardware Company was also growing, and the owner of the lot played one company against the other, each of us raising our bid, with the result that in order to secure this lot we were obliged to pay $80.00

per foot front. As the highest price up to that time in that neighborhood had been $50.00 per foot front, we felt we were paying an enormous price for this piece of property. In February we gave James W. Sheehan $4,500.00 in cash and our note at 6% for three years for the balance, $3,500.00. As there was quite a large piece of land immediately west of the Cleveland Hardware Company, which they felt they could purchase at any time, they refused to raise our bid. Afterwards when it became necessary for them to enlarge, they were obliged to pay $85.00 per foot for the piece which they purchased.

Up to this time twist drills had been put on the market without any external finish, and as a rule they were rather a rough looking tool. The practice had been to take the tools from the tempering fires, brush off the dirt and oil which accumulated on them during the tempering process, and send them to market without polishing the surfaces. Early in 1892, I thought it would be a good stroke of business to run a leather wheel with fine emery on it through the flutes of the drill, and to buff the outside surface. We put this into practice, so that at the opening of the World's Fair at Chicago in 1893 we were putting on the market a much finer finished product than any of our competitors. I went to Chicago and had the firm of A. H. Andrews build us quite a large booth with ample showcases all round the sides, so that the tools could be inspected from either the outside or the inside of the booth. At the Fair we exhibited the largest collection of twist drills and tools that had ever been shown at any exhibition. We took pains to have in the showcases placards stating that these goods were taken right from our stockroom without any attempt to finish them specially for exhibition purposes, and that our customers could depend upon getting goods of the same finish at all times.

The other exhibitors of twist drills had been in the habit of putting a high polish on all goods for exhibition purposes but furnishing to their customers the dull, dirty, unfinished articles.

About six months after the close of the Fair one of our traveling salesmen was told by a hardware dealer that a salesman from one of our competitors had been in his store quite recently. The dealer told him he did not want any of his goods as ours were finished so much finer. The salesman replied that was all humbug, that the finished goods he had were part of our Chicago exhibit. Thereupon the dealer said, "They must have had a damned big exhibit then, as I have been getting that finish regularly for more than a year."

During the progress of the Fair, Mrs. Cox and I went with the two boys to Chicago and spent two weeks, stopping at the house of Mrs. C. E. Conover on Kimbark Street. Mrs. Conover was an old friend of Nellie's and had thrown her house open during the Fair for the use of her friends and acquaintances. She was an excellent housekeeper and we enjoyed the visit there immensely.

On July 1 I went to Magnolia as usual with my family to spend two months at the seashore. On leaving home, I said to Mr. Prentiss that everything was in good shape and he would have no trouble in handling the business, as we had a bank balance, over and above all current indebtedness, of $25,000.00. If business should continue for the next two months as it had been during the year, the balance would show a gain instead of a loss.

Up to July 1 our sales were $11,203.00 larger for 1893 than

they had been for the previous year, which up to that time was the best year we ever had.

I left for the seashore therefore with a light heart, feeling no anxiety for the business. We had been at Magnolia but a few days when the great financial panic of '93 swept over the country, and Frank wrote me that although we had plenty of money on hand, the banks refused to cash our checks, and as we could not get money to pay the men, he would have to close the factory. This he was most reluctantly forced to do.

Our sales, which for the first six months had averaged over $12,000.00 per month, suddenly dropped off to $6,600.00 for July, and $4,600.00 for August.

Earlier in the year my attention had been called to a socket for holding twist drills which had been invented by a Mr. Andrew of Cincinnati. He wanted to sell us his patent and I went down to Cincinnati to see him and examine his socket or chuck. He wanted $10,000.00 for his invention. I felt that we could not afford to pay any such price for such a device, told him so and returned to Cleveland.

His device had some merit. Feeling that it would be desirable for The Cleveland Twist Drill Company to have something similar to it, I gave the subject considerable thought. I finally devised a grip socket different from Andrew's, and in most respects superior to it. I applied for a patent on this grip socket, but before the patent was allowed, our salesmen were insistent that I should give them samples of the socket as well as printed matter about it so that they could begin the active sale of it. I did not think this was a safe procedure, but finally yielded to their earnest entreaties and we sent out circulars all over the country giving a full description of the socket. The circular was marked "Patent Applied For."

Mr. Andrew took one of these circulars to his attorney in Cincinnati and applied for a patent on identically the same device, claiming priority of invention. This led to a long legal conflict between us. In the end we defeated him in every instance and the patent was granted to us on October 15, 1895.

Our foreman in the machine shop, W. T. Armstrong, had made the first socket according to my sketches and suggested some alteration in the shape of the key used in it. So the patent was taken out in the joint name of Cox & Armstrong.

The Franklin Institute of Philadelphia, without any solicitation on my part and, in fact, without my knowledge, investigated the socket, acting through its committee on Science and Arts. The committee in its report said, "This socket is well made, of good design, and of much value. It permits the use of drills and other tools that have become useless in the ordinary socket, holding the tool in place when the pressure is either pushing or pulling on the same, thus making it valuable for many kinds of work." The Institute awarded the Edward Longstreth Medal of Merit to the inventors, J. D. Cox and William Telfer Armstrong, on April 18, 1896.

For many years our western representative, Mr. W. C. Brown, had urged us to manufacture and put on the market a line of goods known as wood bits. These tools, having square taper shanks to fit the carpenter's bit brace, were much longer than the ordinary bit stock drills and had long, tapering points. The principal users of such tools were wagon makers and blacksmiths. Early in this year we bought a Bradley hammer and built a small wooden building adjoining the large blacksmith shop which was in the middle of our premises. Jos. Dyson & Son, who did a general forging and blacksmith business, had rented a small portion of our lot and had erected at their own expense this forge shop, in which they had a small engine for running their blowers.

We connected our shaft to this engine and in this way obtained power to run our hammer, and commenced the manufacture of wood bits. This power proved to be insufficient for our work, so in September, 1894, we purchased and installed a gas engine.

We had been paying up our debts as rapidly as possible during 1892 and '93, so that on January 1, 1894, we were owing but $2,953.00. Most of this was for the purchases for the month of December, 1893.

As an item of interest, I insert below a letter which I wrote in 1903 to my sons, Houghton and Jacob, who were then at college, about one of the notes I had given Judge Prentiss in 1880. It shows what a long, tedious pull it was to pay up our indebtedness to him. Endorsements on the back of the note showed each payment as it was made.

Judge Prentiss loaned us money repeatedly without any security beyond the firm's note. He was always deeply interested in the business and would inquire every few days how we were getting on. He always expressed his confidence that ultimately we would build up a large business. I feel our success was largely due to the fact that Judge Prentiss had confidence in us and loaned us freely of his means to carry on. It has always been a source of gratification to me to know that before his death we paid every cent of our debt to him. Here is the letter:

January 28, 1903

Dear Boys,

I had occasion to go to my drawer in the office safe today and I came across the enclosed note for $2,000.00 made to Judge Prentiss in 1880. This money was borrowed to help carry on the Twist Drill business. I have always kept it for two reasons—one because it is an interesting souvenir of the early days of the business, the other was to show it some day to you boys—to impress on you how hard it is to pay up money once borrowed. You will notice on the back of the note that I could not pay the interest—that no endorsements were made after 1882 till 1888. This is a silent reminder of hard times and the fierce struggle for existence which I went through when you boys were babies. I was forced to the most extreme economies and had hammered into me by daily experiences the necessity of economy in small things. Habits thus ground into one's very existence are hard to overcome, and this long process has left its scars on my mental growth—which will account for the shocks I get when I see what I think is extravagance in others, especially my sons, who don't realize what an awful experience I went through accumulating the means that to them seem to come so easily and freely now. The foundation that carries the skyscraper that attracts the eye of every passer-by—is laid far down in the earth—no one sees that. So with successes in life—every one sees and admires a brilliant success, but few, very few, know anything of the long years of struggle that laid the foundation which made that success possible.

This note was one of many—the rest I destroyed as I paid them off—at one time the firm was owing the Judge $45,000.00. We paid it all off before he died and have never since that time owed a cent we couldn't pay at sight. It took, as you see, nearly 14 years to pay this little note of $2,000.00. We are giving our checks for many times this amount every week now and think nothing of it. The foundation for a splendid business is laid—and well laid. It remains for you boys to build on it a fitting superstructure. That will require judgment, good sense, diligence and close application. I hope you will prove equal to the task and leave to your children a monument that they can feel proud of—and ambitious to carry on to still grander results. This business was begun by me—I borrowed $2,000.00, which was *all* the capital it ever had. I was personally responsible for that $2,000.00, so the business did not owe even that. In 26 years we have increased that until this first of January in 1903 our assets are close to $1,000,000. To equal that performance you have no small job ahead of you—and to do less will not satisfy your self-esteem.

Good night

Return the note to me.   Papa.

Ships in Cleveland Harbor, 1892

PART VI

ATTAINING SUCCESS

*W*HILE business had not been as good during 1893 as in 1892, yet we felt that the new finish on our product would insure us a large increase in business when the effects of the panic of '93 would be overcome and business resume its normal proportions.

As we could not increase our facilities to any great extent in our present buildings, we had Captain Levi T. Scofield draw up plans for an addition to the factory on the Lake Street front. This building was to be 110 feet long on Lake Street and 40 feet deep. We intended to use the first floor for our stockroom and shipping room, and as our stock of goods on hand was increasing in value, we arranged to have this room fireproof, the floor and ceiling made of brick arches thoroughly cemented. The two upper floors were of mill construction. The first layer of the floor consisted of strips five inches wide by two inches thick laid on edge, each strip spiked to the one previously laid. On top of this was ⅞ inch matched flooring laid diagonally and thoroughly nailed down to the five-inch pieces below. On top of this was laid one-inch narrow maple flooring, thoroughly nailed to that underneath. This made the total thickness of the floor seven inches. As there were no joists, it left a clean ceiling underneath and was a type of construction thoroughly approved by the Underwriters.

We put in a good basement, and built the whole building unusually strong so that at any future time we could add to it one or more stories. This building was completed, ready for occupancy by March, 1895. This gave us triple the floor space we had originally on this site.

Shortly after the commencement of this Lake Street addition, we heard from several parts of the country that the traveling men of one of our competitors were spreading the story that The Cleveland Twist Drill Company was about to go into receivership. We were very indignant at this report, but paid little attention to it, except to instruct our salesmen to advise everyone that we were *not* going into receivership, but were practically doubling our facilities for doing business.

In the fall of 1894, Mr. H. A. Garfield came to me and asked me if I would work with him and some other gentlemen, mutual friends of ours, to form a trust company, under the Ohio law passed May 16, 1894. Mr. Garfield's idea was to have a large number of representative business men as stockholders in the company and to limit the amount of stock for which any one of them might subscribe to $10,000.00 par value.

As I felt I had all the work on my hands that I could take care of, I consented on the condition that I should not be asked to take any position of responsibility in the new company.

A few days after this interview, Mr. Garfield, Mr. R. A. Harman, Mr. A. B. McNairy, Mr. Charles L. Pack, and myself had a meeting and went over a long list of representative men in the city, dividing the list up, each one agreeing to see a certain number of the gentlemen whose names were on the list. It was discouraging work at first, as this form of company was a new one in Ohio and everyone thought there were as many banks in the city as the city needed. Also everyone was feeling more or less poor, owing to the financial setback of 1893. But after continued and persistent efforts we succeeded in getting the stock all subscribed for. In September, 1894, we incorporated under the name of The Cleveland Trust Company and formed a temporary organization, the following gentlemen being elected directors.

Luther Allen	H. Clark Ford	J. M. Henderson
F. L. Alcott	H. A. Garfield	A. B. McNairy
Edmund Clark	M. S. Greenough	Charles L. Pack
J. D. Cox	R. A. Harman	H. A. Sherwin

The capital stock was $500,000.00 and each subscriber paid $120.00 per share. This extra $20.00 was paid in as a surplus, so that we might comply with the law requiring trust companies to deposit with the Secretary of State securities to the amount of $100,000.00. This was a new feature in stock subscriptions at that time and excited a great deal of comment.

When the permanent organization was effected in January, 1895, I was asked to accept the position of vice president, but absolutely declined to do so, and also declined to serve on the executive committee. I was, however, very much interested in the new company and frequently attended the meetings of the executive committee, where I was of assistance to the committee through my knowledge of the manufacturing business.

About a year after the organization of the company, there was a vacancy on the executive committee owing to the resignation of one of the members who had become interested in the organization of a rival company to be known as the Western Reserve Trust Company. I was asked to fill this vacancy on the executive committee and did so and remained a member of the executive committee for many years.

As soon as our new building was completed, in 1895, we

moved all of the machinery that was on the second floor of the old building into the new building and used a large part of the second floor of the old building for office space. We moved the finished stock into the new building and built and purchased new machinery, greatly enlarging our facilities both in the factory and the office.

Since 1882, Mr. James D. Foot, 101 Chambers Street, New York, had represented us in New York and New England, selling our goods on commission. We furnished him a complete stock of our tools. Mr. Foot was the president of the Kearney & Foot File Company, who were file manufacturers. At his request we had given him the agency for the eastern states, as he wanted to sell drills in connection with his files and could do so at very little additional expense to himself while the profits to him would be quite large.

For two or three years I had felt that it was a mistake for us to have our goods in the hands of agents to sell on commission. I believed that we ought to be represented by our own men, who would sell our goods exclusively and devote all their time to building up our business. During 1894, I had talked with Mr. Prentiss about my idea of taking our goods out of Mr. Foot's hands, but Mr. Prentiss thought he was doing well enough and that it would be best for us not to disturb our relations with him.

After returns of the business of 1894 were all in, I went carefully over the sales made by Mr. Foot since he had taken our agency, and satisfied myself that he was not pushing the business as he should. His sales were getting smaller instead of larger. Mr. Prentiss had sailed for Australia in January, 1895, and could not be reached. I disliked very much to take any decided action in this matter, knowing as I did that

Mr. Prentiss was in favor of letting it rest as it was. But the more I thought of it, the more convinced I became in my own mind that we would make a mistake to continue with Mr. Foot any longer. So in April I went to New York and had an interview with Mr. Foot. I showed him that his sales were decreasing while the company's total sales were rapidly increasing, and told him I felt the time had come when we should have our own office in New York.

Mr. Foot wanted me to pay him $2,500.00 for the good will which he had established, offering in that case to turn over to us all the correspondence, copy books, etc., pertaining to the drill business. If we would not pay him, he would retain this correspondence. We would not know who his customers were and would be obliged to spend a good deal of money to recover the lost ground. I asked a day's time to consider the subject. After thinking about it overnight, I concluded that in all probability his customers were only such as bought files of him, and that as he had not conducted the business energetically, it would be folly for me to pay him a large sum for his good will. I therefore decided not to pay him anything, but to start in by ourselves and work up a new business.

After giving Mr. Foot my decision, I spent a day or two in New York looking for a store, and succeeded in renting one-half of a large store at 99 Reade Street, the balance of the store being occupied by Wooley & Baynon, who were hardware dealers. I took measurements of the floor space, made a memorandum of them, and returned to Cleveland. Immediately upon my return, I engaged a carpenter and gave him sketches of counters and cupboards for the stock. I had this work pushed to the utmost, with the result that in fifteen days the counters, cupboards and everything were finished, and we shipped to New York two carloads of furnishings and stock for our new store. We had everything set in place and the store ready for business May 1, 1895.

My first intention had been to have all of the stock which Mr. Foot had on hand packed in boxes and delivered to our new store. But I found that Mr. Foot was delaying the packing of these goods unnecessarily and that if I were to depend upon him, we would not have any stock in our store on May 1 when we wished to open it. So without changing my orders to him, I packed up a complete stock at Cleveland, shipped it with the counters and cases and surprised Mr. Foot by opening up on May 1 with everything complete, including a fine stock of tools. I then advised Mr. Foot to ship his stock back to Cleveland, which he did. Our sales from New York declined for a couple of months, but after that were larger than before and increased rapidly. This was the beginning of our series of stockrooms located in the principal centers of the country.

When Mr. Prentiss returned from Australia he visited our New York store. He complimented me upon the change and was always an enthusiastic supporter of this project.

We had for some years been doing an export business through the house of Selig, Sonnenthal & Company, London, but were ambitious to extend our export business. We believed we had made a mistake in allowing Selig, Sonnenthal & Company to have control of our entire European business. Mr. Prentiss had made a trip to Europe in March, 1892, and again in 1895 on his way to Australia, with the result that we began to ship goods into Russia in 1896.

Very early in the history of our business, a Mr. Durfy of Bridgeport, Connecticut, called upon me in the interest of an inventor who had procured a patent on a twist drill with small tubes let in on each side to convey oil from the shank down to the lip of the drill. I told Mr. Durfy that I thought the invention had merit but that my experience in the business satisfied me that there was such a limited demand for tools of that kind that it would not pay us to invest any money in a patent. By 1896 the bicycle industry had grown to such proportions that it became necessary to use the very best appliances in every stage of the work in order to produce the bicycles rapidly and economically. An important part of the cost of building a bicycle was making the hubs. These were turned down from solid material and usually bored in the same machine. As the patents on oil tube drills had expired, we were among the first to manufacture and sell drills with oil tubes in them for this job. We soon acquired a wide reputation for that class of tools and were the first to publish, in this year, a list of sizes and prices.

I invented a socket for holding drills fitted with oil tubes arranged in such a way that oil could be conveyed through the socket into the tubes in the drill while the drill and socket were revolving. This was a long step in advance of the previous practice where oil tube drills had been used in turret head machines in which the work revolved and the drill was stationary. I applied for patents on this socket and secured two patents on November 23, 1897.

One day Bardons & Oliver, of this city, who were large manufacturers of bicycle hubs and also of machinery for making them, telephoned me to come over to their shop. On my arrival I found that they had built a large and improved machine for making bicycle hubs, by means of which they could shave the outside of the hub to size and shape much more rapidly than they could drill the hole. The problem which they wanted me to help them solve was how to drill the hole faster. The hubs were about four inches long. The problem therefore was how to drill a one-inch hole four inches deep while the shaving tools were forming the outside of the hub. The hubs were made in what is called a screw machine, the stock being held in a hollow spindle chuck.

Two shaving tools were used, one on the front and one on the back, these tools approaching each other slowly, while a drill held in the turret head was forced through the center. As the shaving tools had to be exceedingly sharp in order to produce a smooth finished job, there was a limit to the speed or number of revolutions per minute which could be used. I saw at once that if they could revolve the stock more rapidly they could drill the holes faster, but the number of revolutions which they could give the stock was limited to the endurance of the fine edge of the shaving tools. Both Mr. Bardons and Mr. Oliver said emphatically that they had reached the limit in that direction. I said to them, "The only thing that you can possibly do is revolve your drill by means of some contrivance." After a few moments' thought, I suggested to them that they arrange a shaft above the work with gears on either end of it, one gear to be driven by the gears in the head stock of the machine, and the other gear to drive a pinion placed on the shank of the drill. The idea appealed to them and in a few days I was called again to their plant to see it operate.

By this simple contrivance they were able to increase the output of each hub machine from 45 to 80 hubs per day. I told them they had not yet reached the limit of the endurance of the drills and they could afford to run the drills still faster, as they were still not drilling the hubs as fast as they could shave them. In the next machine they built for making bicycle hubs they arranged to revolve the drill by means of a vertical shaft run with bevel gears from the counter shaft above. With this machine they increased their output from 80 hubs per day to considerably over a hundred. This was the speed limit, since they were now drilling the hubs in the same time it took to shave them. Repeatedly we received orders from them for oil tube drills from one inch to $1\frac{1}{4}$ inch diameter. These drills would stand this excessive work five hours continuously. Thus, by grinding the drills in the morning and at noon, the machines could run all day.

In 1897 a few of the most progressive men in the Chamber of Commerce thought that the Chamber ought to have its own building. After a good deal of agitation on the subject, a meeting was called and a committee of fifteen or twenty members was appointed to consider ways and means for accomplishing that objective. I was put on that committee. It met by the call of the chairman and the majority of the committee seemed to be in favor of a stock company. The stock was to be subscribed for by the members of the Chamber, each one to take as much stock as he chose. This idea did not appeal to me, as I felt that many valuable members would not be able to subscribe for much stock and some members might want to take large blocks of this stock, and eventually the result would be that a few of the larger stockholders would control the Chamber. I felt this would be very undesirable. The meeting broke up without anything definite being settled. I immediately went to the chairman of the committee and told him what I thought of the stock company scheme. I suggested that a better plan would be to sell seats in the Chamber, each member being required to buy one seat. For those members who felt they were able to give more than $100, we could have life members, and for those who were able to give still more money, we could have honorary members. My plan met with the approval of the chairman of the committee. He said, "You put that in writing and present it at our next meeting, and I will do all I can to put it through." Immediately I sat down and wrote out my plan, which was as follows:

First: Each member of the Chamber of Commerce must buy a membership seat at $100.00 and pay $25.00 dues annually.

Second: A limited number of life memberships should be created, not over 200, at $500.00 each, such life memberships to be free from dues and to be transferable.

Third: That a few honorary memberships be created at $1,000.00 each, such memberships to be free from dues, non-transferable, and to expire with the death of the holder.

This I handed to the chairman, and at the next meeting I proposed this scheme to the committee. In advocating the life membership class, I argued that any man who contemplated remaining in the Chamber indefinitely could afford to buy a $500.00 membership seat, because he would practically have to set aside $500.00 per year at 5% to pay his $25.00 annual dues. Therefore, it would be to the advantage of such as could afford it to pay $500.00 down to buy a life membership. I figured there were enough members in the Chamber who could be made to see the advantage of this class of membership to raise the money needed for the building.

This plan was adopted and the committee at once set to work canvassing the members for the sale of seats. As soon as enough signatures were obtained to insure a sufficient sum, the land on the north side of the Public Square was purchased and, when a further sufficient sum was pledged, the building committee was appointed and the building erected. It was dedicated in May, 1899. We were not able to raise quite enough cash to complete the building, so bonds for about $45,000.00 were issued.

In April, 1898, I was elected a member of the Board of Directors of the Chamber of Commerce for one year, and re-elected April, 1899.

The custom previous to this year had been, when the Board of Directors first met, to have nominations made for president, vice-president, treasurer and secretary. Then these officers were elected by calling for the ayes and noes. At the first meeting of the directors in 1899, it was felt that such a proceeding might be embarrassing, so each director was requested to write the name he would prefer on a slip of paper. All slips were placed in a hat and counted by a teller. The result of this was that I received the largest number of votes cast. I realized that on the next vote I would in all probability be elected. I did not wish to assume the responsibilities of the presidency of the Chamber, so I arose and said that I felt I could not accept the vote if tendered to me, and I would gladly withdraw in favor of Mr. Greenough, who had the next highest number of votes, if the gentlemen who had voted for me would consent to the change. My friends objected to this at first, but consented to cast their votes for Mr. Greenough for president if I would accept the position of vice-president. This I agreed to do, and Mr. Greenough was unanimously elected on the next ballot. I was elected first vice-president and chairman of the executive committee. As

Mr. Greenough spent several months in Europe during 1899, I acted as president during his absence.

In December, 1897, Mr. Prentiss made his second trip to Australia. The first one was a great disappointment, as he was unable, through the excessive conservatism of Australian buyers, to make any sales. Australia had never been visited before by a representative of a twist drill manufacturing concern. As Mr. Prentiss was very thorough with his work and had a large assortment of fine samples, which he distributed freely, not only to the dealers but to the consumers throughout the colonies, he had made a good impression. On his second trip he was received cordially and heartily by all whom he had visited the first time. The result was that we became the largest furnishers of twist drills to the Australian Colonies.

We added two more hammers to our forge shop in 1897 and found that the gas engine which we had purchased to run the forge shop was wholly inadequate for the work. Gas engines were being introduced in many factories at this time. I had hoped that the solution of the growth of our factory so far as power was concerned, would be satisfactorily solved by putting individual gas engines in each department, as we needed more power. Each engine would be sufficient to run the department in which it was placed. Several factories that I was acquainted with had proceeded along these lines with apparent success.

About this time, electricity as a motive power was being developed. When our gas engine had to be removed from the forge shop, we installed in its place an electric motor, connecting it with a generator in the near-by factory of the Brown Hoisting Machinery Company, paying them for power used. This motor worked very satisfactorily, and early in 1898 we installed another motor in our turning department. The engine purchased of the Ingersoll Milling Machine Company had reached its limit.

When we purchased the lot west of us, we gave a certain gentleman a lease for office space on the land and switching facilities for a coal yard. Later when we built the Lake Street addition in 1894 and '95, we transferred the gentleman from the Lake Street lot to the rear of our original lot on Kirtland Street, giving him a lease there for his office building and use of the switch tracks. I drew up the lease myself in duplicate, and specified that we lease him a strip of track 160 feet from the *southeast* corner of our property, but the track in fact extended clear across the end of the Kirtland Street lot, across the next lot, and down its west side to Lake Street, a total of about 500 feet. He had had the use of this track from 1895 to 1898, although his lease covered only 160 feet from Kirtland Street.

Our sales had grown from $121,936.00 in 1894 to $181,718.00 in 1897, or nearly 50 per cent in three years. We therefore thought it advisable to erect a new building on the west side of our property, and had plans drawn for a large building 275 feet long by 40 feet wide, three stories high. When completed this would give us six times the floor space we had had ten years previously. We notified the gentleman that under the terms of the lease we would expect him to discontinue use of the track beyond the 160 feet specified. He took his copy of the lease and altered it to read 160 feet from the *southwest* corner of our property, and engaged an attorney to prevent our ousting him from the use of the track. Unless we could move the railroad track, we could not put up the desired building.

I took my copy of the lease, which I had had recorded, to H. A. Garfield and asked him what we had better do.

The gentleman, through his attorney, offered to vacate the premises on the payment of $1,000.00. Acting on the advice of Mr. Garfield, we did so. Mr. Garfield said they could enjoin us from going ahead with the building and tie the matter up in court long enough to greatly inconvenience us, though he thought we could without doubt win our suit in the end. Rather than go to this delay and fight it out, we paid the thousand dollars and commenced our No. 4 building in November, 1898.

During this year I designed, and we built in the factory, a four spindle drilling machine for drilling the malleable iron shanks for bit stock drills. This machine was unique, but simple in design, the drills protruding up through the surface plate. The malleable shanks were held in a suitable holder over the drills and were fed down by weights. My object in building the machine in this way was to get rid of the chips which in malleable iron get very hot and stick to the drills and soon spoil them. This machine was very successful and was used continuously until we began the forging of such drills from the solid bar.

In the spring of 1898, I bought the thirty-foot cutter yacht "Vashti" for $1,800.00, trading my yacht "Cy-Pres" in part payment. The "Vashti" was built in 1888 by George Lawley of Boston after his own designs. Every one who has seen her has conceded her to be the most comfortable, roomy yacht of her size on the Atlantic Coast. She was built of the very best material in the strongest possible manner, and, so far as I can judge, is as sound today (1905) as she ever was.

The detail work of the office at this time had reached a

point where I felt that I must get someone to help me. I was looking after the traveling men, doing all the correspondence, had charge of the office force and shipping department, and every minute of the day was so fully occupied that I could

Left: Father and myself—crew of the "Vashti"

Below: The 30-foot cutter yacht "Vashti" as she sailed the Atlantic Ocean

not give the attention to the improvement of machinery, etc., that I felt the business needed.

Mr. E. G. Buckwell of Knoxville, Tennessee, who had purchased goods from us, was passing through the city in the summer of 1898, and called upon us. He stated at that time that if in the future any opening should arise in our business, he wished we would consider him as an applicant. After discussing the subject with Mr. Prentiss, who agreed with me that we needed more help in the office, I corresponded with

E. G. Buckwell

him and as a result he agreed in November of 1898 to come with us on January 1 to take the position of sales manager. Mr. Buckwell had a fine personality and had had thorough training in sales work. He was an ideal man for the job and devoted himself energetically and successfully to expanding our sales outlets. He has won many friends for us in the trade and cemented our relations with our dealers on a basis of mutual respect and confidence.

Our new house on Euclid Avenue was finished and ready for occupancy in the fall of 1899, and on Thanksgiving Day,

Our new home on Euclid Avenue, built in 1899

as it was the Golden Wedding Anniversary of father and mother, we had a family reunion. Nearly all the family were present, including the grandchildren. We had a merry time, ending up the festivities with father and mother leading the Virginia Reel. The children presented father and mother with a Golden Loving Cup with the dates of the marriage and "Golden Wedding" engraved on it.

We made a contract in January, 1899, to equip our factory throughout with the latest fire sprinkling arrangement. By installing this sprinkling system we reduced our insurance from $2.50 a thousand to $1.60. In February we gave a contract for a new engine, and in July broke ground for the building of a modern power house which had been completely designed and engineered by the George S. Rider Company, consulting engineers. It was the last word in industrial power plants for that time, with overhead coal bunkers and complete mechanical equipment for handling the coal and conveying it to the fires, so that no hand labor was necessary at any time.

When we commenced the west wing of the factory (No. 4 Bldg.) in 1898, we decided to furnish it with the most modern and best sanitary appliances. We put in ample facilities for washing, supplying the wash basins with soap and towels. On the completion of the building, we opened a restaurant in the top story so that every noon the men could have hot dinners. We felt that too many of the men were going off at noon to the corner saloons for beer and sandwiches and that better work would be done by them if they could have a hot lunch with coffee. We also equipped the factory with open-work iron lockers so that each man could have a place for his clothes and lunch basket.

When we served our first lunch on November 29, 1899, it took us forty-five minutes to serve the tables after the men sat down. It looked as though we had undertaken something which would be very difficult to accomplish. However, by a little planning we succeeded after a short time in serving the tables promptly. We arranged the workmen in groups, assigning nine men to each table, but placing only eight seats to a table; the odd man, who was elected by each group, was allowed to leave his work fifteen minutes before noon. These men, one from each table, immediately assembled in the dining room and served the soup, bread and butter and coffee to the tables. This consumed about all of the fifteen minutes allowed them, and they were ready upon the seating of the workmen to distribute the meat, vegetables and dessert. This arrangement worked so satisfactorily that by the end of twenty minutes the workmen were ready to leave the tables.

In order to keep the men in the factory and to encourage their desire for reading, we established a reading room in

Reading room, a service to employees

which we placed all of the popular illustrated magazines, many scientific and trade papers, besides two copies each of the morning papers. We also decorated the walls of the reading room with maps of the world showing the telegraph, railroad and steamship routes.

We also started at this time a night school, which we kept up for two or three years, until the Y.M.C.A. undertook similar work. We employed teachers, and any of the workmen who wished could join these classes. English was taught, as were mathematics and mechanical drawing. For those who attended the night school, we served a supper in the dining

*Night school was provided where shop personnel learned
mathematics and mechanical drawing*

room. Many of the young men made rapid progress in mathematics and mechanical drawing, and we were able later to pick out bright, intelligent men for promotions to the best jobs in the factory.

By February, 1900, we had our new power house completed and the wiring of the factory finished, and on the 15th of the

*In 1900 this power house supplied electricity for operating
equipment and lighting*

month turned on the power for the entire factory. The next day, February 16, the engine was wrecked. The crosshead broke in two, and the pistons were blown through the cylinder covers. Fortunately, no one was hurt.

That the men appreciated the advanced provisions for their comfort and convenience, is evident from the fact that on August 21, 1900, we were presented with a voluntary testimonial signed by one hundred and ninety-five of them, reading as follows:

"We, the undersigned, in the employ of the Cleveland Twist Drill Company, grateful for the many comforts and conveniences so thoughtfully and generously provided by the firm, take this method of expressing our thanks for the same, together with a sincere wish for the continued prosperity of Cox and Prentiss."   Cleveland, Ohio, Aug.21st,1900.

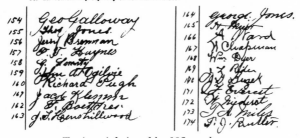

Testimonial signed by 195 employees

A few years previous a new competitor had appeared in Taunton, Massachusetts, under the name "The T & B Twist Drill Company." These letters were the initials of the two principals—Tweedy and Burchard. They manufactured some very nice looking drills. The milling was particularly good, and it was evident that someone in their organization was a good mechanic and designer. But their capital was inadequate, and after a year or two they were glad to sell out to the Morse Company in New Bedford.

I was finding it more and more difficult to give any time to the designing of machinery, yet was conscious that there was a great deal which we ought to be doing to improve our

E. C. Peck

methods and equipment. Progress never ceases, and if we meant to lead the procession, as we did, it was necessary to have some first-class designing talent working steadily at that job.

I still had in my thoughts the desirability of an automatic machine for milling twist drills, and believed that it could be accomplished if some one of high grade mechanical ability could be given the opportunity to concentrate on the problem. Mr. Prentiss and I talked it over and concluded that the man who had designed the equipment for the T & B Company would be a good man for us, if we could find out who he was. After some searching we located our man in the person of Mr. E. C. Peck, who was then employed by the Card Tap & Die Company of Mansfield, Massachusetts. Mr. Peck, we learned,

General office and switchboard as it appeared in 1900

had had a wide experience in the twist drill business, having worked for Whitman & Barnes at Akron before going with T & B. After they sold out to Morse, he spent some months with the Morse Company. Mr. Prentiss made a trip to Mansfield in March, 1900, and succeeded in signing up Mr. Peck to come with us as designing engineer. He proved to be an excellent selection—a most capable mechanic and versatile designer. Under his able administration the improvement of our mechanical equipment has been going forward with rapid and steady strides.

In September of this year we completed handsome new offices, which had been remodeled under the plans and supervision of Mr. C. F. Schweinfurth, Cleveland's leading architect, who designed Trinity Cathedral and many of Cleveland's finest residences.

On October 18 our engine again broke down in the same way as the first time. Both accidents were due to the fact that the manufacturers had furnished us a cast iron crosshead when the specifications called for steel. We tried in vain to get the engine builders to stand the expense of the breakdown, but they refused. We immediately let a contract for a new engine to a different builder, the Ball & Wood Company of Elizabethport, New Jersey.

In November, I applied for a patent on a socket, the drift hole of which had its upper walls inclined towards the center so that the drift when inserted in a socket would lie squarely on the end of the drill. The object was to prevent battering the corners of the drill tangs. This patent was granted in March, 1901, and we have continued to manufacture all of our sockets in this way ever since.

A young man by the name of Morse, a graduate of Cornell University, had invented and patented what was probably the first electrically operated optical pyrometer. He called it the Morse Heat Gage, and undertook to manufacture and sell it. This instrument consisted of a tube in which was mounted a small, closely coiled, spiral filament very much like the hairspring of a watch. Through this filament was passed a carefully regulated electric current which heated the filament to whatever temperature was desired. By looking through the tube, one could compare the color of the red hot filament with the color of a tool in the hardening furnace. When the filament disappeared from view against the background of the tool, because the colors were identical, the temperatures were then identical also. By means of this device the temperature of the tools in the hardening furnace could be accurately known and regulated to within two to five degrees Fahrenheit. This was an almost unbelievable advance over anything previously known. Hitherto we had been compelled to rely on the judgment, experience and skill of the hardener who, in turn, depended on the constantly variable color sense of the unaided human eye.

When Mr. Morse demonstrated and explained his instrument, I saw at once what a tremendous help it could be to us in attaining uniform quality, and what an advantage we might gain over our competitors if we could acquire exclusive rights to his invention. We therefore promptly entered into negotiations with him and shortly succeeded in acquiring the exclusive right to his invention for the twist drill industry. On November 25, 1900, we installed the Morse Heat Gage and soon had applied it to all the heat treating operations throughout the factory. I have always considered this to be one of the most important steps we ever took towards the maintenance of the utmost quality in our product. I believe it has been and will continue to be, over the years, of the greatest advantage to our company in its competitive struggle.

On October 17, 1901, we turned steam into our new Ball & Wood engine, and it has continued to run very satisfactorily to this time (1905).

In this same month, October, 1901, we opened our second stockroom at Chicago. We felt that there was a great deal of business in Chicago which we were not securing, and we also thought that by carrying a good stock of our tools there we could more quickly and more satisfactorily supply our Western customers. The results have been very satisfactory.

In January, 1902, we put in a large screw machine, built by Bardons & Oliver, but with special features of my own suggestion, by means of which we could turn the outside of sockets, and drill and ream the holes in them at the same time. This machine saved a large per cent of the cost of making sockets. This operation was still further improved by an automatic machine in 1905.

We commenced our No. 5 Building during the month of October, 1902. This building extended from the old Ingersoll shop down to the power house. It was three stories plus a basement, with sufficiently heavy foundations so that in the future we could add one or two more stories to it. It was completed in January, 1903, at which time we gave a dance in the new building for our employees.

The latter part of 1902 I took up the question of taper bridge reamers with Mr. Peck, telling him I believed we could mill the taper and straight part all in one cut, thus saving a great deal of time in their manufacture. Mr. Peck studied the problem and designed an attachment to go on our milling machines. The desired results were accomplished, and we afterwards put a special attachment on some of our lathes so that the taper and straight part were turned in one cut. This enabled us to turn out these taper bridge reamers at much less cost.

Mr. Peck meanwhile had designed an automatic milling machine, and on December 11, 1903, the first machine was completed and ready to work. This machine was constructed so that the blanks were fed to the chuck from a hopper. The flutes were milled in one head, then the blank was swung around and the back clearance was milled on a second head. This machine worked without a stop or hitch of any kind from the very first day.

Jacob D. Cox, Sr., founder, and Jacob D. Cox, Jr.

Thus, a project of twenty years was at last brought to successful fruition. The new machine not only milled the flutes automatically, but the back clearance also, thus performing the two most difficult and costly operations in making a drill at one and the same time. The reduction in cost thus achieved is sufficient to earn a good profit on each drill produced, even though all the rest of the work should have to be done at cost.

In August, 1904, Mr. Peck completed an automatic machine for stamping size, name, and trademark on straight shank drill blanks. This has been a very successful machine in every way.

In December, 1904, after more than thirty-five years of strenuous work, I felt I had earned the right to retire, so I suggested to Mr. Prentiss that we incorporate our company and elect him president. This plan was carried out, and Cox and Prentiss turned over to the incorporated company on January 1, 1905, a million dollars in assets over and above all liabilities.

On Our Seventy-fifth Anniversary

$\mathcal{B}$Y 1905 The Cleveland Twist Drill Company had gained leadership in manufacturing twist drills and reamers. With the broad foundation laid down by its founder, Jacob Dolson Cox, Sr., it had a firm base on which to grow and expand.

Through the years, many of Mr. Cox's early principles of maintaining superior manufacturing facilities and good industrial relations, coupled with adequate distribution and sound sales policies, have made it possible to build the organization as it is today. Methods constantly have been improved, machines modernized, and necessary additions built. As each change was made, careful consideration was given to insure "better tools at lower cost."

In the past forty-six years we have had good times and bad times, as well as the extreme demands on our facilities

〖 178 〗

THE
CLEVELAND
TWIST DRILL COMPANY
CLEVELAND OHIO, U.S.A.
NEW YORK, DETROIT, CHICAGO,
DALLAS, SAN FRANCISCO, LOS ANGELES,
Established, 1876

brought about by two world wars. We have faced these conditions with the same courage and determination that Mr. Cox put forth in the early years of the company between 1876 and 1905.

Today our facilities comprise ten acres of manufacturing floor space, including 19 buildings. To accomplish the task of manufacturing and stocking ten thousand different types, styles and sizes of regular tools, plus many thousands of special tools, we utilize more than 3000 machines.

To provide adequate service for our more than 800 distributors, we now have six stockrooms located in the major metalworking centers of the country. Each stockroom carries a complete line of tools and assists the distributors in the territory it covers.

〖 179 〗